400 Group Games and Activities for Teaching Math

Other Books by the Authors:

Creative Units for the Elementary School Teacher
Parker Publishing Co. Inc., 1969

Edward F. DeRoche

Erika Gierl Bogenschild

400 Group Games and Activities for Teaching Math

Parker Publishing Company Inc. West Nyack, N.Y.

Library of Congress Cataloging in Publication Data

DeRoche, Edward F
    400 group games and activities for teaching math.

    1. Mathematics--Study and teaching (Elementary)
I. Bogenschild, Erika Gierl   joint
author. II. Title.
QA135.5.D47   372.7   77-2816
ISBN 0-13-329847-7

Printed in the United States of America

The Scope and Practical Value
of This Book

Guiding group activities in the classroom is one of the major tasks that teachers face. The teacher's ability to utilize group activities as a means of helping youngsters achieve social and academic skills remains one of education's most important functions. In today's mathematics classrooms, group instruction continues to be the most often used pattern of teaching and learning. Teachers use group patterns because they find that it meets the needs of busy and productive teaching-learning situations. Teachers use group methods of instruction in mathematics because they have discovered that it actually helps individualize instruction.

In the real world of the classroom, it is only fair for teachers, facing the day-to-day problems of teaching and learning, to ask: "How can we individualize instruction? There are thirty children to every one of us!" It may seem unrealistic to suggest that one individual responsible for thirty eager, energetic, different human beings can attempt to meet the needs of these children in all subject matter areas, including mathematics.

This book will convince you there *is* a way it can be done. In sports it is called the "team effort." Every member of a sports team, as you know, is responsible for the success or failure of the team and the individuals on that team. The whole idea of team sports is to get individual members working together to achieve goals, namely, winning games. Using this idea in the classroom, the teacher becomes a "learning manager"—organizing his or her classroom so that the atmosphere and activities promote a "team effort" among the learners. Each new math task, skill or concept to be learned becomes a game—a challenge. The team—the class— along with the learning manager—the teacher—prepares a "game plan."

This book will demonstrate how teachers can develop "game plans" for helping children learn math skills. The idea of promoting a team effort among children in class and attacking math tasks, skills and concepts with a specific plan is based upon two valid and time-tested principles of learning—namely, "if you want to learn something well, teach it," and "nothing succeeds like success."

Using the ideas in this book, you will find that pupils can learn mathematical skills in small groups, develop independence in learning and, equally important, develop a positive attitude towards the subject. Group patterns, properly used, will not only help facilitate learning but should reduce individual competition and potential conflict. In other words, math skills will be learned in conjunction with social skills. Just as pupils learn responsibility by being held responsible, they learn to work in groups by being in groups designed to accomplish specific tasks. Group work encourages cooperation—a concern for the achievement and progress of others. Group work promotes leadership qualities of pupils. It is through the process of group work that pupils learn to share their ideas, skills and talents.

The essential objectives of group work, and the theme that permeates the strategies and activities in this book are as follows:

- Group work helps youngsters learn to carry out delegated responsibilities.
- It helps youngsters achieve a sense of accomplishment.
- It develops essential life-long social skills.
- It promotes leadership abilities.
- It demonstrates the principles of democratic problem-solving.

The four hundred math strategies and activities in this unique read-to-use resource book not only promote these objectives, but they illustrate a practical and meaningful procedure for individualizing instruction as well. The math activities in each chapter of this book provide suggestions for teaching and learning in:

- small groups
- team learning patterns
- peer teaching patterns
- special interest groups
- remedial groups
- project groups
- self-help groups
- independent study groups.

This book is for teachers who want to try new teaching strategies. It is a book for the busy teacher who needs resources that have been classroom tested, that save time and effort, and that "turn pupils on" to math. It is a book for teachers who care about human relationships among their pupils and who believe that pupils can learn mathematical skills and concepts while learning the human skills of cooperation, tolerance, patience, understanding, respect and competence. Therefore, this book is for all elementary and junior high school teachers, regardless of grade level, who want to improve their ability to teach math and promote a positive, more productive classroom climate.

How To Use This Book

If it's fun, can it be learning? The mathematical activities in this book are designed to answer this question affirmatively. The four hundred activities are based upon some practical ideas about teaching and learning.

1. Learning the skills and concepts in math should be enjoyable.
2. The learner should understand the practical implications of learning math. Some call it relevance; others suggest that it answers the question "Why do we have to learn this?"

3. Teachers should assign their lessons so that children proceed from concrete experiences to abstract concepts.
4. Learners learn by doing—by being actively engaged in the process of learning math.
5. "Nothing succeeds like success" may be a cliché, but in learning math it means that children need to find their experiences rewarding, satisfying and challenging.
6. The teacher should establish a classroom atmosphere that encourages cooperation and concern for each other's learning—where children, individually and in groups, are given choices in their methods, materials and activities in learning math.

In essence, this is what this book is all about. This is why four hundred learning activities, using a variety of materials, emphasizing a non-textbook method of learning math skills and concepts, have been written.

The Group Way

This book emphasizes group activities for the learning of mathematics skills and concepts.

Group methods of instruction, group cooperation and competition, the "team effort," should help each teacher toward the goal of individualizing instruction. When groups of children are working diligently and cooperatively, the teacher has much more time to single out children needing individual attention.

Each chapter provides forty group activities. Yet the teacher in arranging the class for group instruction should decide whether to use:

1. small groups: 3 or 4 children for each activity;
2. peer learning patterns: where one youngster teaches one or two other youngsters;
3. team learning patterns: one team carries out several activities and then reports to other groups or the entire class. The reporting, however, should be done in creative fashion, utilizing a variety of methods, i.e. the use of cassette tapes, overhead projector, making their own filmstrip, etc.

4. special interest groups: certain groups of children may discover other activities they would like to explore after completing one or more activities in this book. Teachers should encourage children to go beyond the activities they are completing, to suggest other avenues of exploration and to identify additional activities that they should be accomplishing.

5. remedial groups: children who have difficulty learning a skill, understanding a concept, or accomplishing one or more of the activities can be brought together in a group for instruction by the teacher and to help each other learn what is giving them difficulty;

6. project groups: some children will prefer one or more activities in each of these chapters to some other activities. The teacher should give children the opportunity to select projects or activities of primary interest to them. All activities do not have to be completed by all children.

7. self-help groups: much like remedial groups, except that teachers can employ self-help groups as teacher-aides; that is, one group helps another group with a task or activity.

8. independent study groups: are made up of children who can proceed with little or no direction from the teacher. For example, children in independent study groups may complete, throughout the year, all of the activities described in chapter ten. The teacher's main task is to determine how they will report the results of their activities and how they will be evaluated.

Suggestions for Using the Activities in This Book

Obviously, this book does not include all the learning activities in mathematics. Each chapter provides forty activities aimed to serve the needs of all grade levels. Yet each teacher should answer the following questions:

a. Are my children capable of carrying out this activity successfully?

b. Do the activities in each chapter provide ideas that I can adapt or adopt?

c. As I read each chapter, or try out selected activities, what additional ideas can I think of that may be of equal value to my children?

This book should not be used chapter by chapter except in the case of unit teaching. For example, if a teacher is teaching a unit on the metric system or the origin of numbers, then it is possible to utilize all of the activities in each chapter on that particular topic.

Otherwise, a better method is to select activities that will supplement the content of the textbook or that will enable both teacher and learner to accomplish the objectives of the unit or lesson. For example, a teacher preparing lessons on sets would have to scan each chapter to determine what activities might be usable. There may be two or more activities on sets in chapter three (geometric shapes), in chapter six (newspapers) and in chapter eight (games).

In summary, a teacher determines the objectives of the unit or lesson and the method of instruction (group and/or individual), and then plans procedures that will include the activities in this book.

Edward F. DeRoche
Erika Gierl Bogenschild

Contents

14

When one thinks of enrichment one thinks of an individual, a gifted student. This chapter provides forty enrichment activities for both individuals and groups. Here is the chapter teachers can use for those groups that can "go beyond" grade level math work.

Complete List
of
Games and Activities

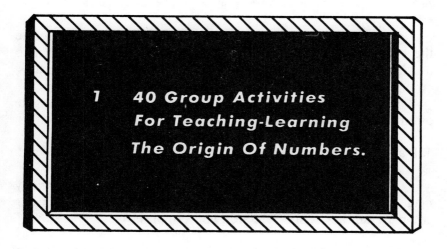

1 40 Group Activities For Teaching-Learning The Origin Of Numbers.

Man probably first started using numbers when he began trading with his neighbors. Counting was necessary and, since man needed something to count with, he used fingers and toes, stones and pebbles, sticks and tally marks.

As time passed, and man started recording the many occurrences in his world, he needed an easier more accurate way of doing this recording.

About five thousand years ago, written numbers began to appear in Egypt and Mesopotamia. The Egyptian priests started recording on what was called a papyrus. The Mesopotamians recorded on soft clay. The number system used by the Egyptians was simply a stroke for each number for 1 to 9; for 10 they used his symbol ∩; for 100, ℮.

The Romans, three thousand years later, used the same strokes for numbers 1 to 4, but used V for 5, X for 10, L for 50, and C for 100. By adding a stroke (I) to V, they could write a symbol for the value of 6. A V and two strokes represented the value 7.

The Mayas of Central America used a dot, a stroke and an oval in their number system. Using dots and strokes, they could write numbers from one to nineteen. For example, a dot represented number one, four dots represented number four. A stroke represented number five. A stroke with a dot over it (÷) represented number six. Two strokes (=) represented the value of ten.

Our so-called Arabic number system originated long before the systems just described. The Hindus of India were the first to use the position of a numeral to indicate the value (units, tens, etc.). They also introduced the use of zero.

The following activities will encourage learners to investigate our number system, its origin and development.

1. Making an Abacus (Groups of two or three students)

Have each group read about abaci or handle a commercially made abacus. Then ask each group to make their own abacus using any material they wish. Here are two examples:

(A) *Egg carton abacus:* staple two egg cartons together so that there are four rows of pockets. Cut off three or four rows so that you have nine vertical rows. Label the first row ONES, second row TENS and so on. Use marbles as counters.

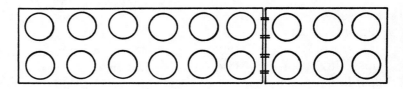

(B) Another easy way for youngsters to make an abacus is to use a piece of wood or cardboard, tacks, string and beads.
Place the tacks in the wood as shown; tie the string to one of the tacks; bead the string; tie the other end of the string to the tacks.

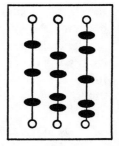

Each team should prepare two or three problems that the other team can solve using their abaci. When each team is finished using the abaci, they may wish to donate them to the kindergarten or first grade classes!

2. Numeration (Special Interest Groups)

Students will find the methods of counting using symbols or letters of ancient civilizations interesting.

Arrange the class in special interest groups to complete the following chart:

Civilizations	Time	Counting System Used
Sumerians	5000 years ago	base 60—cuneiform
Babylonians		
Egyptians		
Greeks		
Romans		
Hindus		
Mayas		
Arabs		

3. Numeration—continued

Have each of the groups design teaching strategies for explaining the numeration system of the civilization they studied. Encourage a variety of ways of reporting to the class using cassette tapes, the overhead projector, sandwich boards, skits, and so on.

4. Number Shorthand (Class)

Prepare a ditto of the following chart (excluding the answers).

NUMBER SHORTHAND

TERM	MATHEMATICAL SYMBOL	ANSWER
Infinity	_____	∞
Squaring	_____	n^2
Degree	_____	n^o
Addition	_____	$+$

Subtraction	_____	-
Multiplication	_____	x
Division	_____	÷
Equals	_____	=
Therefore	_____	∴
More than	_____	>
Less than	_____	<
Not less than	_____	≮
Intersection	_____	∩
Not equal to	_____	≠
Union	_____	∪
A subset of	_____	⊆
Less than or equal to	_____	≤
Greater than or equal to	_____	≥
Similar to	_____	~

Each student is to supply as many answers as he knows without using references. Then he/she is to go around to other members of the class to complete those not known. After this procedure has been completed, record all those symbols on the board that no one knew the answer to. Have two or more students find the meaning of these symbols and report to the class. Discuss with the class the purpose of mathematic symbols.

5. Symbol Bingo (Class)

Select members of the class to prepare bingo cards with a variety of symbols on them. Example:

+	n^2	∞
≤	−	≥
∩	∴	X

∪	÷	⊆
<	~	>
≠	∞	n^2

Cut an old deck of playing cards in half. Cut pieces of white construction paper to be glued over the face of each half-card. Using a felt pen draw on the mathematic symbols (make approximately five cards per symbol). Place in a box. Shake! Pass out the bingo cards. Play the game!

6. Famous Mathmaticians (Special Interest Groups)

Have each group select a name from the following list and investigate contributions of each person by answering questions that follow the list of names.

Varahamihira	Archimedes
Eratosthenes	Pythagoras
Aryabhata	Euclid
Leibnitz	Pascal

(A) Who was this person?

(B) When did he live? Where did he live?

(C) What did he do for a living?

(D) What was his contribution to mathematics?

7. Math Words (Class activity)

Prepare a ditto handout as shown below for use in math and spelling class.

Word	Your Definition	Dictionary or Math Book Definition
Abacus		
Associative		
Chord		
Closure		
Commutative		
Digit		
Distributive		
Factor		

Word	Your Definition	Dictionary or Math Book Definition
Integer		
Notation		
Number		
Numeral		
Property		
Ratio		
Reciprocal		
Set		
Subset		

8. Number Lines (Small groups of three of four students)

Have each group prepare number lines of the Aztec, Mayan, Roman, Egyptian, binary, etc. numeration systems.

For example, using pinch-type clothespins and string, one group of students might illustrate Roman numeration as follows:

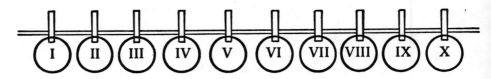

Using these number lines, each group can make up two or three problems to solve on another's number line.

9. Computers (Independent Study)

Some students may be interested in computer mathematics. The binary system (base two) is used because the computer uses two symbols, one (on) and zero (off). Sometimes octonal (base eight) is used.

    (a) Have individual students investigate how computers are used in their community. Report results to the entire class.

(b) Other students can interview computer programmers and prepare a tape of the interview for the class.

(c) Some students can show the class how the numbers in the decimal system are converted to the binary system.

(d) One or two students can explain the use of the IBM card and how data is punched on this card.

10. Bulletin Board Collage (Class activity)

Have students prepare a collage of pictures, numbers, words, items and objects to illustrate how numbers influence our lives.

11. Binary Birthdays (Class activity)

Prepare a large chart on which students write their names, their birthdates and the translation of the date into the binary system; then in the final column, have each student select an ancient numeration system (Roman, Greek, Aztec, etc.) as shown:

Name	Birthdate	Binary System	Ancient System
John Doe	7/7/64	111/111/1000000	Roman VII/VII/LXIV

12. Book List (Special Interest Group)

Have this group prepare a list of books related to the topics in this chapter that they feel other students in class would like to read. Have this group read the books first and then prepare posters on each book. On the list might be such books as:

Adler, Irving. *Numbers Old and New.* New York: John Day Co., 1960.

Bendick, Jeanne. *Take A Number.* New York: McGraw Hill, 1961.

Carona, Philip. *The True Book of Numbers.* Chicago: Children's Press, 1964.

13. Project Probe (Project groups of four or five students)

In order to build the pyramids, the Egyptian architects had

to know much about mathematics, particularly geometry (meter—to measure).

Have groups of students volunteer to probe into the construction, mathematical principles and background of such phenomena as the Pyramids, Stonehenge, etc.

14. Number Names (Class Project)

Give each student a sheet of 8½ x 11 paper. Have them fold it in half and then fold the half in half so that when it is open there are four sections on each side of the paper.

Give each student a number—any number—and have him/her write eight different names for that number. For number 4, for example

4	Four
2 + 2	5 − 1

Quadrant	Quartet
3 + 1	8 − 4

15. "Cross-Math Puzzles" (Remedial Groups)

Have teams of 2-3 students who have difficulty with particular math skills or concepts make simple cross-math puzzles. This procedure enables the student to design cross-math puzzles in an area in which he/she needs remedial help, and at the same time he/she can complete the puzzles of others.

Here is an example of a simple cross-math puzzle on numbers.

Down	ACROSS
(A) 1	(B) Fingers
(B) Trio	(C) >
(C) to find your height and weight	(D) Rhymes with ATE
(E) numbers added up or the sum	(E) Quartet

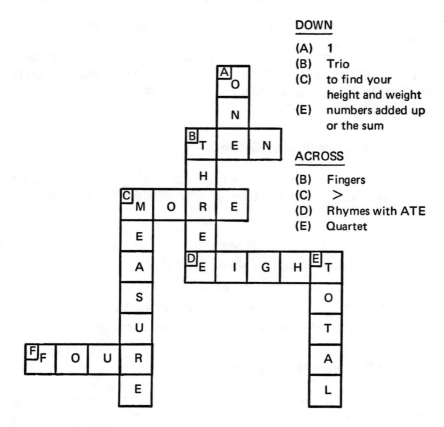

DOWN

(A)   1
(B)   Trio
(C)   to find your
         height and weight
(E)   numbers added up
         or the sum

ACROSS

(B)   Fingers
(C)   >
(D)   Rhymes with ATE
(E)   Quartet

16. Number Systems (Small Groups and Team Learning)

Have each group devise its own numeration system.

Each group must then demonstrate its numeration system to the class.

Following the demonstration, the group has students pair off into problem-solving teams and provides each team with one or two problems based on the numeration system they have demonstrated.

17. Number Sequency (Remedial Groups)

For students having difficulty understanding the sequences of numbers, decks of playing cards can be helpful. Ask the students to bring in old decks of cards. Remove the face cards; use aces as ones. Have each youngster in the remedial group shuffle the cards and deal out about five cards, face up on the desk.

Ask each student to put the card that shows the smallest number on his/her left and the card that shows the largest amount number on his/her right. Then place the other three cards between these two in proper sequence.

18. Number Lines (Project Groups)

Have each group select one or more of the following from which they are to construct number lines using any material they wish.

(a) number of days in each month

(b) birthdays and dates of classmates

(c) number of months in a decade

(d) number of years in a decade, century, etc.

(e) number of pupils in each grade in the school

19. Counting Clues (Small group)

Students can work with numbers larger than nine by using counting boxes. For example, each team can collect popsicle sticks, poker chips, buttons, etc., and two small boxes which should be labeled "ones" and "tens." The material should be bundled in groups of ten and placed in the appropriate box; the material left over is placed in the "ones" box.

Each group of students should prepare one or two problems based on the material they have and invite other groups to their desk to try to solve the problems.

20. Number Patterns (Self-help groups)

Students who seem to have difficulty with numeration, number patterns, addition, subtraction, multiplication, and/or division can be helped by self-help groups (teacher aides) to design activities similar to the following example for students needing assistance in this area.

Example:

(A) 1   2   3   4 = 10   What sign is used?
(B) (1   2)   3   4 = 9   What signs are used?
(C) 1   2   3   4 = 8   (Answer -1 + 2 + 3 + 4 = 8)

21. Ancient Clocks (Project groups 2-3 students)

Have each group of students select one of the following styles in making clocks that will be displayed on the bulletin board or as mobiles:

Roman numerals, binary system, Aztec numeration, Egyptian numeration, Sumerian numeration (cuneiform), etc.

22. Number Lore (Special interest groups—two or three students)

Ancient cultures believed in the magic powers of numbers. Today, some people believe that certain numbers are lucky and unlucky.

Have students in special interest groups investigate the "lore" and "expression" that deal with numbers. Here are a few that they can start with:

(a) 7 and 11 as lucky numbers;

(b) 13 is unlucky; in certain tall buildings no floor is numbered 13;

(c) to the ancient Greeks, even numbers were thought of as breakable, weak, feminine; odd numbers, unbreakable, strong, masculine; 5 represented marriage—the union of 2 and 3, the first feminine and first masculine number.

(d) three cheers; seventh heaven; things in sixes and sevens.

23. What's the Rule? (Entire class)

Prepare a handout for each youngster in class. The purpose of this activity is to help students discover number patterns (reasoning) and the rules used to form the pattern.

Name _____ Date _____

WHAT'S THE RULE?

1. SEQUENCE: 1, 2, 3, 4, 5, 6, ___ , ___ .
   RULE: (answer: add 1 to previous term)
2. SEQUENCE: 2, 4, 6, 8, 10, ___ , 14.
   RULE: (answer: add 2 to previous term)
3. SEQUENCE: 2, 4, 16, 256, ____ , ____ .
   RULE: (answer: square the previous term)
4. SEQUENCE: 1, 4, 9, 16, 25, ___ .
   RULE: (answer: square each consecutive whole number, beginning with 1)
5. SEQUENCE: 8, 16, 24, 32, ___ , ___ .
   RULE: (Multiply initial term by sequence beginning with 2; the eight table)

24. Number Sentence (Remedial or self-help groups)

Have groups make a series of activity cards to help others to understand addition and subtraction by making number sentences. Each group can decide what procedure they will use for making number sentences. Some may want to draw their own; others may want to cut pictures from magazines. Here are three examples:

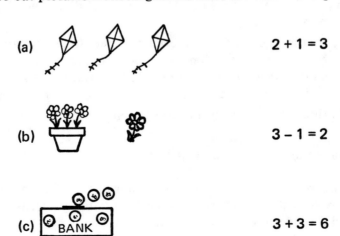

(a)   2 + 1 = 3

(b)   3 − 1 = 2

(c)   3 + 3 = 6

25. What Does It Mean? (Entire class)

Following are three principles of the decimal system that each student should understand—either by rewriting in his/her own words and/or illustrating the principle.

Give each student a sheet of paper. After you have projected (using the overhead projector) each principle on the screen, read it to the class, having them follow along with you. You may reread it with the class as many times as you wish.

After reading each principle three or four times, have the students rewrite it in their own words or illustrate the principle in some way. Only three principles are stated—check your math book (teacher's edition) for additional principles.

Principle 1: In a place-value system of numeration, the value of a digit is the product of the number by the digit and the value of the place.

Principle 2: In a numeration system based on the place-value principle, there are no symbols for the group values.

Principle 3: In a place-value system each symbol in a numeral has a *form* value and a *place* value.

26. Math Charades (Entire class)

Have each child select a card from a paper bag with some statement relative to numbers, numeration, etc. Have them act it out and the class try to guess what statement was on the card. Here are a few examples of statements for the cards:

1. Roman numerals
2. unlucky 13
3. snake eyes (dice—two ones)
4. $8 + 9 = 17$
5. $10 - 5 = 5$
6. channel 4
7. eight and ate
8. group by ones and tens
9. midnight
10. your telephone number

27. Place Holder Chart (Class or small groups)

		Hundred Thousands	Ten Thousands	Thousands	Hundreds			Decimal Point		Hundreths	Thousandths	Ten Thousandths

Millions · Hundred Thousands · Ten Thousands · Thousands · Hundreds · Tens · Ones · Decimal Point · Tenths · Hundreths · Thousandths · Ten Thousandths

When children learn the concept that numbers, no matter how large, are place holders, the reading and use of these place holders will be more easily understood.

Reproduce this graph on the board or on mimeo and allow each child to place various numbers on the chart.

More gifted children can handle larger numbers.

28. Group Abacus (Class)

Have the class line up in groups representing ones, tens, hundreds, etc. The teacher then calls out a number (example: 1, 341). At this time the students, representing the correct numbers from each row, step up to a predetermined line. Shift students from line to line and row to row to allow each a chance to represent a different place holder.

29. Number Lines (Class or small groups)

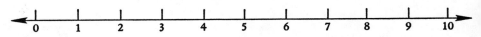

1. Compare the two number lines and rename a list of numbers as Roman numerals. Example:

   10 =

   3 =

$7 =$

$8 =$

$9 =$

$1 =$

$5 =$

2. Did the Romans have a symbol for zero? What did they use in its place?

3. How did the Romans indicate 4, 6 and 9?

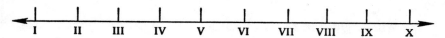

| I | II | III | IV | V | VI | VII | VIII | IX | X |

30. Egyptian and Roman Symbols (Class or small groups)

Numbers		Symbols
1	_____	1
10	_____	∩
100	_____	?
1000	_____	🌷
1,000,000	_____	👤
10	_____	X
1	_____	I
5	_____	V

Directions:

1. Write the symbol for 50 using the Egyptian symbols.

2. Write the number for _____ .

3. Write the number eleven using a combination of the two systems.

4. Try simple addition, subtraction or multiplication using the two systems.

5. Make up problems using these systems.

31. Card Counting (Groups of three to six)

Card games such as 21 (Black Jack), are valuable tools for the teaching of addition. Discuss values of cards and rules of game: aces equal 1 or 11; 2 through 10 are face value; picture cards equal ten.

The object of the game is to beat the dealer (teacher or another student) without going over 21. When beating the dealer, the winner takes over the deal.

Any card game which stresses counting can be used.

32. Numerical Order: Binary System (Class)

Experiment:

With eight three-by-five cards, make a set of "punch cards" that shows exactly how the binary system is used for sorting cards. Cut four holes near the top of one card and repeat for the other seven cards. Number the cards and make notches as shown on the following example. The pattern of notches and holes on each card will correspond to the binary way of writing the large number on the face of each card. To demonstrate how the cards are sorted, mix the cards thoroughly and form them into a packet resembling a deck of cards. Push a pencil through the fourth opening and lift the pencil up. Some cards will be lifted, and some will be left behind. Shake the deck to make sure that all the cards that are supposed to drop off do. Lift up and pull out of the deck all of the cards that hang on to the pencil. Place those cards in front of the other cards. Repeat this procedure inserting the pencil in the third opening, then again in the second opening, and finally in the first opening. After the last sorting, the cards will be in numerical order.

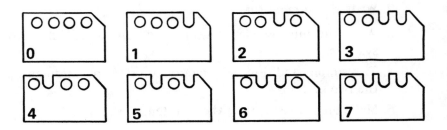

For an extra challenge, enlarge the deck.

33. Numeration-System Matching (Class)

To start the activity, place a pile of picture cards on a table and beside it place a stack of tally-mark cutouts and a stack of numeral cutouts. Instruct a pupil to take the first picture card, find the tally-mark cutouts that belong to each picture, and fasten them to the card. The pupil should then find the correct numeral cutout to complete the match.

34. Symbols +, -, x, ÷, =, ≠, ( ), >, < (Teams)

Place on the chalk ledge any or all of a set of cards containing the following symbols (+, -, x, ÷, =, ≠, ( ), >, <). Call upon pupils to do one of the following.

(a) Choose a card and give the name of the symbol and its meaning;

(b) choose a card and give the name of the symbol and use it in an example;

(c) play a game with two teams in which a member of Team A explain the use of a symbol and a member of Team B finds it.

35. Numerals—Coded Numbers

Some ancient people like the Greeks used the letters of their alphabet as their names for numbers. Use our alphabet to name numbers. Make up a code such as the one below. Write letter symbols and figure out the number using the code chart.

(a) Use the code to develop number problems.

(b) Have students develop their own code.

1	A	10	J	100	S
2	B	20	K	200	T
3	C	30	L	300	U
4	D	40	M	400	V

5	E	50	N	500	W
6	F	60	O	600	X
7	G	70	P	700	Y
8	H	80	Q	800	Z
9	I	90	R	900	*

36. Numeral Breakdown

As a challenging activity for abler students, suggest that they discover as many ways as they can to write such numerals as 99, 87, 76, etc., to represent a rearrangement of tens and ones. They might make a chart. This activity can be extended to hundreds, thousands, etc.

		tens	ones
99		9	9
		8	19
		7	29
		6	39
		etc.	

37. Counting and Recognizing Numbers

(a) Have several children each day count the number of boys and girls in attendance. Each child should be touched as he is counted. During the day, count the number of children in reading groups, play groups, at lunch tables, etc.

(b) Have children count the chairs, tables, milk bottles, blocks, papers, crayons, pencils, rhythm instruments, erasers, beats in music, trees, flowers, pages in a book, etc. as a result of needs, incidental or planned. Use the various forms of counting (cardinal, ordinal, grouping).

(c) Have children draw balls, balloons, milk bottles, flowers, cups, pennies, according to the teacher's instructions such as "Draw three cups. Color two red."

(d) Have children string a given number of beads.

(e) Have children place a given number of blocks in a row and/or arrange in number families.

(f) Have children take a given number of steps.

(g) Supply each child with sticks or other small objects and ask him/her to arrange a given number into his/her own choosing.

(h) Give each child a set of number cards which he/she is to arrange in order on his/her desk.

(i) Arrange a play supermarket with pictures of groceries or empty cartons and cans. Children then go to the store to look for counting possibilities and then go back to their desks to arrange markers to indicate numbers found, as, three markers to show that three cans of milk were found on the store shelves, etc.

(j) Write number-names on the board. Call on children one at a time to read a word and erase it. Begin with the poorest readers so they may select the ones they know.

(k) Have children illustrate number "stories." For example, a child may draw a tree with four pears on it to show that he/she knows how many four is.

(l) Have children tell their house numbers, telephone numbers, street numbers, ages, birthdates.

(m) Have pupils estimate the number of children in a group, blocks in a pile, milk bottles on the table, steps to the door, windows in the school building, etc.

(n) Whisper to a child to go outside the room and rap on the door a certain number of times. The other children listen and when called upon, tell how many knocks they heard.

38. Equations (Teams)

Have student(s) make up their own "scramble" (ex.: 1, 4, 8, 13, +, -, +), for another to accept as a challenge to unscramble $(8 + 4 = 13 - 1)$. Variation—"Scramble" a term.

39. Understanding Terms

Call upon a pupil to define a term; ask another pupil to name the term, e.g., a) "It may be interpreted as repeated addition of the same number", b) "Multiplication." Or ask a pupil to name a term; ask another pupil to exemplify it.

40. Numeral Chart (Class)

As a culminating activity, the study of numbers could be expressed by using two-figure numerals from 1 to 99.

	10	20	30	40	50	60	70	80	90
1	11	21	31	41	51	61	71	81	91
2	12	22	32	42	52	62	72	82	92
3	13	23	33	43	53	63	73	83	93
4	14	24	34	44	54	64	74	84	94
5	15	25	35	45	55	65	75	85	95
6	16	26	36	46	56	66	76	86	96
7	17	27	37	47	57	67	77	87	97
8	18	28	38	48	58	68	78	88	98
9	19	29	39	49	59	69	79	89	99

Ask the class to point out patterns in the chart:

a) Reading horizontally, the number in the "ones row" doesn't change; i.e., it is always the number in the first column.

b) Reading horizontally, the number in the "tens row" is sequenced (1 to 9);

c) Reading vertically, the number in the "ones column" are sequenced (1 to 9);

d) Reading vertically, the numbers in the "tens column" are the same until one reaches the ninth number in the "ones column."

Ask the class to "play around" with the numbers in the chart to find other patterns. For example, in the "ones row" adding the numbers 1-2(3), 2-2(4), 3-2(5), etc. provides a sequential pattern. Reading from number 11 diagonally provides another pattern (11, 22, 33, 44, etc.).

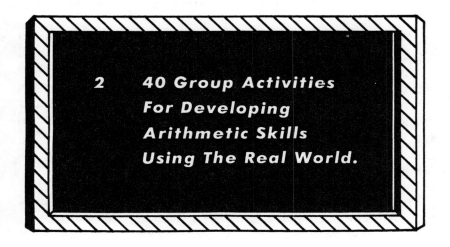

**2   40 Group Activities
For Developing
Arithmetic Skills
Using The Real World.**

How many of your students suffer from what Mitchell Tazaores calls "mathophobia"—the belief that mathematics must be difficult and unpleasant? How many of your students have the opportunity to explore the use of mathematics in the real world? How much of your math or arithmetic class time is spent helping students deal with and possibly solve real-life math problems?

The "new math" tried to show students the underlying principles of math operations, set theory, number base, etc. Recent evidence suggests that students also need a realistic view and practical skills in the use of arithmetic to solve everyday problems. In other words, teachers are being asked to consider those skills that students will need to solve problems in a practical way. The idea of learning from experience and learning to handle problems encountered in the real world is not new—it has been promoted over the years by several outstanding educators.

When writing the group activities for this chapter we looked at the use of numbers and computations in our own daily lives. We were surprised that numbers are so much a part of what we do each day. The forty group activities are merely suggestions—a start for the innumerable things that you can do with math in your classroom.*

---

*We have described ideas for using newspapers to help youngsters learn math in chapter six; thus we avoided repeating many of those "real-life" activities in this chapter.

We have selected group activities that will help your students appreciate the use of numbers in their world. We have designed group activities that will enable learners to develop the math skills necessary for coping with the problems in life. Hopefully, the group activities that follow will in some way contribute towards developing among young learners an appreciation of the theoretical and practical aspects of mathematics.

1. Numbers in Our Lives (Class)

Have the class tell how numbers are used in our daily lives. Make a list of their ideas. Expand on these ideas by questioning and discussing each category. A chart could easily be prepared for this activity. Conclude the discussion on the how of numbers. Example:

ITEM	HOW	NUMBER
Television	Channels	1 through 86
Time	Clocks	1 to 12
Games	Bingo, etc.	1 through 99
Temperature	Thermometers	-20 to 120
Measurement	Quarts, pints	1/4, 1/3, 1/2, etc.
Speed	Speedometers	By 5's, 10's, etc.
Radio	Stations	50 to 160

This chart is not complete. You can explore the use of numbers in each of these categories.

2. Collages (Special Project Groups)

Select three special project groups to design collages that illustrate number use in our daily lives. Have one group make a collage on number use in the home; another on number use in our family business transactions; and a third group on number use in recreation. The "home" group can get pictures from catalogs and advertising brochures. The "recreation" group can use pictures from magazines and travel brochures. The "family business" group can use sample checks, credit cards, stamps and pictures of banks, the post office, etc. Each group should be prepared to answer their classmates' questions about items in the collage.

3. "How-To" Cards (Special Project Groups)

Select about eight of your better students and assign them to one of two groups (four in each group) to help you make How To Cards that other students in the class can use to enhance their math skills and to learn to solve real problems. How To Cards can be made on a variety of topics such as:

How to use a stopwatch

How to compute a discount

How to measure distances

How to finance a car

How to start a checking account

How to buy from a catalog

How to estimate the cost of things

How to read a telephone bill

The card should include a statement of objectives, the procedure, an example, a few problems to solve, and an answer key.

4. Math Facts (Remedial Groups)

Use a deck of playing cards, with face cards removed, to teach various arithmetic skills.

Using a deck of cards for every student, have them play five games of addition (one student doing the adding, the other checking) and then subtraction. Each student should receive 20 cards and randomly play one card from his deck. The game can also be used to provide help with multiplication and division facts.

5. Calendar Collection (Class)

Have all students bring their own calendars. Compare the different calendars that they have. What are their similarities? Differences? Do all calendars give us the same information? Use these calendars for some of the other activities suggested in this chapter.

6. Improving the Calendar (Special interest groups)

Select another group of learners who may be interested in improving the calendar we now use. Have the group complete the following and share their ideas with the class.

List suggestions for improving the calendar. Which of these suggestions do you think would be easiest for people to accept? What is leap year? Why do we add a day to our calendar every four years? Why is our calendar called the Gregorian calendar? What is the International Date Line? How is the International Date Line related to the observatory in Greenwich, England? Have students investigate the World Calendar Plan. What are its advantages and disadvantages? Have a committee find out what a "Perpetual Calendar" is. They should then prepare one and report their findings to the rest of the class. Calendars are based on certain assumptions. Suppose we decide to change to a 13-month calendar. What major changes would we have to make to retain accuracy? Would the number of days change? Have youngsters prepare ɩ 13-month calendar incorporating a set of assumptions.

7. Calendar Math (Small Groups)

Arrange the class into small groups of two or three students in each group. Provide each group with a calendar. Have each group make a chart similar to this one:

Months	Days In Each Month	Holidays In The Month
December	31	
January	31	New Year's Day
	⎯⎯⎯	
Total	365	

Have students list the months with 30 days in them, 31 days, less than 30 days. Use the calendar to find them.

8. Calendar Problems (Small Groups)

Have each group find the answer to the following problems. Arrange for each group to put their answers on the board. When answers differ have each group go back and check their work.

A. What is the sum of numbers represented by the numbers in each Sunday of January? February? Etc.

B. Find the sum of all of the first Saturdays of each month.

C. What is the sum of numbers represented by the following holidays? New Year's Day, St. Valentine's Day, Easter, Mother's Day, Father's Day, and Independence Day?

D. Add all the numbers in a particular month and then subtract the holidays. Example: after adding the days in February, subtract Groundhog Day, Lincoln's birthday, St. Valentine's Day, and Washington's Birthday.

9. Calendar Changes (Small Groups)

Have each group find the changes implied in the questions that follow:

A. The first day of the year in 1966 was Saturday.

B. What was the first day of the year in 1967? 1968?

C. What was the first day of the year in 1960?

D. When is your birthday? Will you be in school that day?

E. The last day of each month falls on what day? Is this true of every year?

F. On what date is the first day of summer? Of winter? Is this true every year? Does the date change? Does the day change?

G. Which month is the shortest of the year? Why do we need a month with only 28 days? Why does this month sometimes have 29 days?

10. Calendar Bingo Game (Class)

Give each student a page from the calendar and some round cardboard markers and crayons. Have them block out five or six numbers of their choice. One student selects numbers (1-31) from a box and, as he calls a number, other class members cover their number with their markers. Bingo results when all the numbers are covered vertically, horizontally or diagonally. This is a fun way to learn the numbers from 1 to 31.

11. Moon Calendar (Special interest groups)

Suggest this activity to a group of students who may be interested in completing it and sharing their findings with their classmates.

Have the group record the phases of the moon for a month. Use blocks on the calendar to record this information as follows:

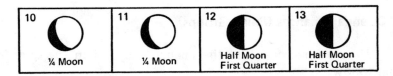

12. Moon Math (Class)

Tell the class that the gravity on the moon is only one-sixth as strong as it is on earth. Have each student make two or three math problems writing each problem on a 3 x 5 card with the answer on the back. Example:

| How much would you weigh on the moon? | How much would a car weigh on the moon? |

Shuffle the cards and have each student select two cards and complete the problems.

13. The Price Is Right Game (Class)

Set up this game following the pattern of the television show by the same name.

Have students prepare for the game by arranging a section of the classroom as the stage with appropriate tables, chairs and other props. Other students can cut material from catalogs and paste them on cards, with the actual price on the back of the card. You, the teacher, can then take these cards and prepare math problems on the back of each card. Other students can select a variety of prizes for winners of the game using travel brochures, etc. For example, one contestant may win a set and is given an all expense paid trip to Hawaii. This contestant then receives a travel brochure to Hawaii.

Have the class select a master or mistress of ceremonies and the rotation of four players for each set until everyone in the class has been scheduled to play the game.

In the classroom version, we can have the students:

(a) try to guess the actual price of the item shown on the card; and/or

(b) estimate to the nearest whole number the price of the item when it is divided by a given number stated on the card; and/or

(c) estimate the price when given a fractional number, e.g. price of a radio is $29.50; estimate one fourth of the actual price. After all of the students have had their turns at being contestants, you can select the winner of each set to be in the "Grand Showcase". This involves estimation of several items without going over the total price. You can add additional calculations by having each contestant estimate the cost of several items and then reducing their guess by seventy percent.

The "Grand Prize" winner goes to lunch with the teacher. The teacher pays.

14. Utility Bills (Special interest group)

Have a group of three or four students collect a sample of water bills, electric bills, telephone bills. Ask this group to prepare three or four charts: one explaining how to read the bill, one on new vocabulary words found on bills—kilowatt, cubic feet, etc., and a third on how the bill to be paid is calculated. Have this group explain their findings to the class.

15. Transportation Schedules (Special interest groups)

Have this group collect all available transportation schedules in their area such as bus, plane, and train schedules.

Have the group study these schedules and prepare a series of learning activities that will show other students in the class how to read each schedule.

Following this activity, ask the group to prepare at least ten realistic problems that their classmates would solve using each schedule.

16. Math Log (Class)

Have each student keep a daily log on their use of mathematics and numbers for one week. They should set up their log so that they make an entry every two hours during the hours that they are awake.

At the end of each day ask them to study their log and make more conclusions based upon the data in the log.

17. Phone Number Booklet (Class)

As a special project and a good method for improving school-community relations, have the class prepare a mimeographed booklet of the important phone numbers that children and parents should have available.

Organize the class into the following committees to complete the tasks assigned.

(a) Typing committee—type material submitted by other other committees (five students).

(b) Collating and final copy committee—put the booklet together, design a cover, staple (five students).

(c) Phone number gathering committees (two or three students per subject): art-entertainment-recreation, consumer affairs, libraries, government officers and offices, utilities, health, schools, emergency, news media.

18. Sports Desk (Special interest group)

Have several special interest groups (three or four students) design scale drawings of the playing areas for a number of sports. Have each group use the same scale (example: $1'' = 10''$) to draw the dimensions of a football and soccer field, volleyball court, baseball diamond, basketball court, softball field. Have them compare their results. What geometric shapes do they find in their drawings?

19. Sports Detective (Project group)

Have a group of four or five youngsters study and investigate the importance of numbers in terms of time, distance and space in the rules of football, track and basketball. For example: What rules relate to the time of a football game? What role do distance and space play in a football game?

20. World Records (Class)

Many people are fascinated by the *Guinness Book Of World Records* (Norris and Ross McWinter, Bantam, 1975, paperback $1.95). Have one or more copies available to the class. Ask each youngster to search out an unusual world record. Each afternoon have two youngsters report to the class on the world record they selected.

Discuss with the class why individuals and groups do the things they do to break some of these records. Also discuss the role that numbers play in these records.

21. Facts and Figures (Class)

The World Almanac and Book of Facts (Newspaper Enterprises Association, paperback, $2.75) is another book that should be of interest to youngsters in your class. There are many ways you can have your class use this valuable resource. One such activity might be called "Fact-Findings." With the assistance of two or more youngsters spend a couple of hours going through the book for problems that you write on a 3 x 5 card with the answer and page number on back of the card or on a separate sheet of paper.

For example:

(A) What is the highway mileage between Boise and Reno?

(B) What is the motto of the state of Nebraska?

(C) Of all the major earthquakes, how many occurred in the U.S.? What percent of the total number of major earthquakes listed is this?

Design about one hundred cards. Each day have each youngster select a card and find the answer. The youngster checks to see if his/her answer is correct. If it is, he/she selects a 3 x 5 card, designs a problem, writes the answer on the card or answer sheet, and places the card in the "Fact-Finding File." If a youngster does not get the answer correct, he/she must, on the next day, find the correct answer, and select another card and complete the problem.

22. Knowing The Community (Class)

Have each member of the class select one of the following so that a profile can be designed about their community, county or neighborhood.

Each student is assigned one item from "Finding The Number Of . . . " list:

(a) elementary students,   (b) middle-junior high students,
(c) senior high students,   (d) teachers,
(e) teacher-student ratio,   (f) principals/other administrators,
(g) schools,   (h) classrooms,
(i) libraries,   (j) banks,
(k) bars,   (l) churches,
(m) theatres,   (n) single-family homes,
(o) multiple-family homes,   (p) apartment houses,
(q) grocery stores,   (r) hardware stores,
(s) barber shops and salons

You may add to this list. Have the class discuss their findings.

23. Things You Wanted To Know About But Were Afraid To Ask (Small groups)

Assign two or three youngsters to each group to explore the use of numbers in the following (one to a group):

(A) Dewey Decimal System
(B) International Dateline
(C) Daylight Savings Time
(D) Balloon Records
(E) Centigrade Scale
(F) Eclipses
(G) Electoral College
(H) Military Time

Have each group prepare material in an interesting way and report their findings to the class. For example, the "Military Time" group could construct two large clocks and show the class how military time compares to our time. They should also have the answer to questions such as "Why do the military have their own methods of stating time?"

24. Income Tax Form (Class)

Obtain a 1040 form for each student in your class. Before completing the form find out from students whether they know who must file the form; what forms should be used; what date is the final date for filing.

Go through each item on the form and have students fill out what they can—example: name, address, filing status, exemptions. Discuss the meaning of each item on the form such as dividends, interest, adjusted gross income, etc.

Discuss the purpose of income taxes—federal and state. You might have a group of students investigate other kinds of taxes—gifts, inheritance, etc.

25. Bank Forms (Class)

Visit your local bank and ask for classroom quantities of the various forms a person might use at a bank—savings slip, deposit slip, withdrawal slip, application for a loan, etc.

Distribute these to the class and go through each form so that students learn how to fill out the forms.

You might then arrange a field trip to the bank to find out how each form is processed.

26. Insurance Forms (Class)

Collect sample insurance policies from local insurance companies for each member of the class. Discuss with the class the purpose of different kinds of insurance—life, home, car, etc. Select a form and discuss some of the terms on the form such as deductible, liability, etc.

Provide the students with an opportunity to fill out an application for an insurance policy.

27. Book And Record Club (Special interest group)

Have two or more special interest groups investigate the

advantages and disadvantages (money, selections, etc.) of belonging to book and/or record clubs over a one-, two- and three-year period.

Have each group prepare an oral report to the class.

28. Let's Go Dining (Class)

Have students collect menus from restaurants in their community. When a variety of menus have been collected, prepare "Dining Out Cards" that include a variety of situations. Here are two examples:

(A) You and two of your friends want to go shopping and eat out rather than returning home. Each of you have $1.05 for meal expenses. Assuming that all of the restaurants are near enough to your shopping area, select one that would best serve your needs. What would be your meal? What is the total cost (don't forget tax)? How much do you have left?

(B) You want to take your father/mother to the movies and dinner for his/her birthday. You have saved $10.75. The movie costs $2.00 for each ticket. From the menus available, select a dinner that you can afford.

29. Weather (Special interest group)

Have a special interest group prepare a display and present a report to the class on how numbers help report weather conditions; include sunrise, sunset, temperature and precipitation data.

30. Computation—Range and Median (Small groups)

Have students write the following numbers on different slips of paper.

(a) the license plate numbers of their parents' cars;

(b) their house numbers;

(c) their telephone numbers;

(d) the number of letters in their first and last names;

(e) their shoe size;

(f) their height (to nearest inch).

Slips in each category should be placed in a small paper box or bag. Have each small group (two or three students) find the range (high to low) and the median (middle score) for the class.

31. Daily Math (Small groups)

Assign each of seven groups a day of the week. Have them individually keep a record of mathematical concepts used during their waking hours—counting, measuring, size, shape, equality, inequality, etc. Each group is to summarize their individual data and prepare a monthly chart on this topic.

32. Dear Math (Class)

Using the pattern of the "Dear Abby" column, give each student an opportunity to write a "Dear Math" problem as follows:

Dear Math: I am sixteen years old and in love with a woman 1½ times my age. Should I ask her to marry me or will she be too old when I'm thirty?

Have the other members of the class write answers to this problem.

33. It's Real (Small groups)

Here are some "big ideas" in mathematics. Either duplicate them or put them on the board.

(a) any order properties of addition and multiplication;

(b) the role of 0 in addition; of 1 in multiplication;

(c) a set is a specific, well defined collection;

(d) relations involve pairing or matching;

(e) a function is a special kind of relation;

(f) an operation is a special kind of function;

(g) graphs show relation and function.

Give one of these "big ideas" to each group. The group should find the meaning of the idea using their math text. The group should also find examples in their text. Their third assignment should be to identify ways the "big idea" is used in everyday life. The group should then share this information with the class.

34. Mail Orders (Class)

Have the students bring in mail order catalogs. Remove the order blanks from these catalogs and duplicate. Give the order blanks to each student. Then, with student help, prepare "learning activity cards" that require "things to do" with each catalog. For example: "Prepare an order required to dress your family for a camping trip." or, "You have $18.50 for presents for your entire family. What will you get each person? Fill out the order blank properly."

35. Post Office (Special interest group)

Have a group of students obtain from their post office information regarding the cost of mailing things according to class (first class, etc.) and other rates (book rate, bulk rate).

Ask them to summarize their information and make a presentation to the class. Also have this group prepare about 50 problems, based on the information they gathered, for others in the class to solve.

36. Zip Code (Special interest group)

Have a group of three or four students prepare an outline map of their city and zone the map according to postal zip codes.

Also have this group prepare an outline map of the United States and find the zip code (first two numbers) for each state.

Ask the group to find out why the post office uses postal zip codes and prepare to report to other members of the class.

37. Yellow Pages (Special interest group)

Have this group study the "civic section" of the Yellow Pages directory and illustrate how numbers are used to tell about their community.

38. Let Your Fingers Do The Problem Solving (Team learning)

Group students into teams of two. Have each team prepare twenty math problems requiring the use of the Yellow Pages directory. Select five problems for each team. Give them five minutes to solve as many problems (correctly) as they can. The winning team does not have to solve the remaining problems. Other teams then complete the problems they did not solve.

Repeat this activity on another day using some or all of the remaining problems.

39. Cereal Boxes (Class)

Have the class bring in a variety of cereal boxes. Have them analyze the box covers for similarities and differences; use of math and numbers; additional advertising; suggestions for use of cereal, etc.

For example: several cereal boxes carry the U.S. Recommended Daily Allowance of essential vitamins. Have the students investigate which cereals give the best nutritional information per serving based on this vitamin list.

Have students compare the cost of the cereals, their ingredients, and the wording (advertising) on the boxes.

40. Product Analysis (Class)

Have the class bring in a variety of labels, boxes, etc. of products their families buy. Use them for computation problems, for comparisons and contrast problems and for content analysis.

For example, one label on a can of soup states—"net wt. 10½ oz. (298 grams)." On an activity card, have students tell what "net wt." means. Then design problems such as: If you bought a case (24 cans) of this soup, what would the "net wt." be for the case?

Another problem: The soup includes among its ingredients "monosodium glutamate, caramel color," etc. What are these used for?

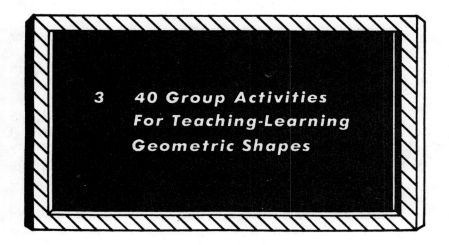

3 40 Group Activities For Teaching-Learning Geometric Shapes

Remember those good old high school days of plane and solid geometry, of axioms, theorems, and postulates:

It may have scared us as students, but as teachers we recognize that the study of geometry can be a great student motivator for the learning of mathematical skills and concepts.

We have written this chapter on geometric shapes for several reasons. The most obvious reason is that geometric shapes are all around us and their study provides numerous opportunities for students to learn how to be observant, how to compare and contrast, how to describe similarities and differences, and how to classify objects according to size, shape and so forth.

We also believe that involving students in learning activities that teach them geometric vocabulary, rules, shapes and definitions is the beginning of a study of geometric concepts that can be refined as they proceed to a more formal study of geometry.

This chapter describes forty activities that actively involve students in explaining the shapes of things around them. We want students to develop their powers of observation and to learn to test conclusions gleaned from these observations.

We based most of the activities on the premise that what we do, we know. We attempted to provide teachers and learners with activities that can be supplemental to what appears in the textbook. In some cases, the activities may be considered pre-textbook material; in others, the activities are clearly designed for enrichment purposes.

1. Strange Shapes (Entire class and teams)

Turn on the overhead projector and place a pencil on it. Ask the students to guess from its shape what the object is. Now try a pair of scissors, a ring, a domino. Can the students identify (visually discriminate) the object from its shape? In addition, have the students verbally identify and/or describe the shape; i.e., circle, square, triangle, etc.

Break the class into teams of two. Have each team find three objects to put on the overhead projector that they feel will stump their classmates. Remember that each team must try to identify the shape first, and then the object. The team that stumps the class the most times out of three opportunities wins. If there are ties, have a "playoff."

2. Shape Collage (Small Groups)

Have groups of students make a colored picture collage (from magazines), identifying each of the following (and more if they can find them): ray, point, segment, plane, solid, square, circle, cone, sphere, triangle, etc.

If you wish to vary this activity, assign each group of three or four students a particular area for collage making: transportation, products, sports, buildings, etc.

3. Reshaping A Product (Small groups)

Have the students work in small groups of three or four to complete the following activity.

Assign each group a product; e.g., an ice cream cone. Ask the group to find an ad or picture of the product, to identify the shapes (ice cream cone: circle and cone) and then to take the product, reshape it and design an ad.

Have each group share its ideas with the class and carefully point out the advantages of the newly shaped product.

4. Shape Sheets (Entire class)

Have each student prepare "shape sheets" using one sheet for

each shape. Each student should label each sheet as follows:
Sheet:

(1) triangle   (2) circle,   (3) polygon,   (4) rhombus,
(5) trapezoid,   (6) hexagon,   (7) parallelogram, (8) plane,
(9) cube,   (10) rectangle

On each sheet, the student should: (a) define the word; (b) draw it; (c) paste on a picture of it; (d) identify a mathematical formula to measure it (e.g., circle: $c = \pi \times d$); (e) summarize one or two points from a math text about it; (f) write a statement about its use in everyday life; (g) tell how you use it (e.g., circle—wheels on my bicycle).

5. Open and Closed Curves (Entire class)

Develop the idea of open and closed curves by giving each youngster a piece of string and have them make opened and closed curves as follows:

OPEN   CLOSED

After instructing children on open and closed curves, have them make examples as shown with the string. Point out that squares, etc. are simple closed curves with segments.

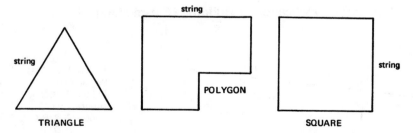

Have the students demonstrate each of the properties of simple closed curves; namely: (1) the points in the interior of the curve, (2) the points in the exterior of the curve, (3) the points on the curve.

6. Shapes and Lines (Entire class)

Have one half the class prepare mimeographed sheets such as the following for their classmates to complete:

Put a red x on the shape that has curved lines and a blue x on the shape that has only straight lines.

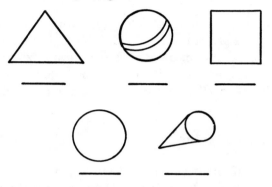

square
cone
sphere
triangle
circle

Find the parallel lines and list them.

A _____

B _____

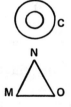

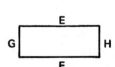

7. Concept and Vocabulary Building (Entire class)

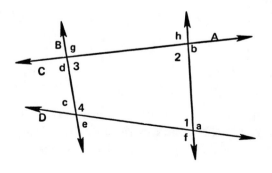

Lines—A, B, C, D
Segments—ab, cd, ef, gh
Points—1, 2, 3, 4
Intersecting
    lines—A-C, B-C, B-D,
        A-D

Develop concepts and vocabulary by introducing *lines, segments, intersections* and *points.*

Worksheets using these concepts may be prepared by the teacher and mimeographed for distribution to the class as follows:

A. Find and mark lines AB, CD, $\overleftrightarrow{AB}$, $\overleftrightarrow{CD}$.

B. Find and mark segments $\overline{ab}$, $\overline{cd}$, $\overline{ef}$, $\overline{gh}$.

C. What lines intersect at point 1? 2? 3? 4?

D. What is the difference between a line, segment and ray?

E. Draw and label each of the following:

$$\overline{AB} \quad \overrightarrow{QR} \quad \overleftrightarrow{ST} \quad \overrightarrow{DE}$$

F. Segments gh are *congruent* with ef because they are equally far apart: if $\overline{gh}$ is *congruent* with $\overline{ef}$ we use the sign ≅ to show this. How, then, would you write this relationship? (Answer: ef ≇ gh)

8. Intersections (Entire class)

Let three sticks have a common point of intersection. Then numerals from 1 to 7 may be placed at the six endpoints and at the intersection so that the sums on all three are equal.

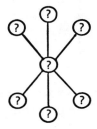   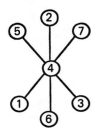

9. Types of Shapes (Entire class)

Discuss types of geometric shapes, the most common of these being rectangles, squares, triangles and circles. Make shapes of colored construction paper or have the youngsters find these shapes in magazines and newspapers and cut them out. Now cut these shapes *apart* and have youngsters reassemble them in order to gain practice in recognizing various geometric shapes. (These figures will be *plane* rather than *solid*.) For example, using numbers, students can cut out patterns as follows:

Let beginners cut apart numerals, letters, or geometric shapes. Reassembly provides a good practice in discrimination of shapes and sizes.

10. Making Geoboards (Entire class)

Have each student make his own geoboard out of styrofoam blocks or corrugated cardboard. Stick in rows of pins or small wooden dowels as shown in the figure.

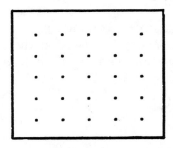

Using string or a rubber band, have students make a series of polygons on their board, one at a time—example: square, rectangle, triangle, hexagon. Have them determine how they would find the perimeter of each.

11. Architects and Shapes (Entire class)

Invite an architect to class to talk about his/her occupation and the importance of shapes in architectural work. Have the class prepare questions in advance; for example, how do architects determine the shapes of buildings? What factors do they consider?

12. Collecting (Small groups)

Divide class into committees and have each committee take a particular geometric shape. Start a collection of objects and/or pictures which exemplify that shape.
Example:

Group   I   CIRCLES—wheels, dishes, ashtrays, some kinds of cereal, pies, etc. (Some youngsters may bring in round objects, which could invite discussion of the differences between *plane* and *solid* figures.)

Group II   SQUARES

Group III   Continue as above, using other shapes.

Set up displays of these collections.

13. Investigation: Entire class

Investigation of these displays will show that certain types of objects have a regular geometric shape for a specific purpose. Further classification for purpose can now be pursued.

Examples:

1. For easy recognition (traffic signs)
2. To make work easier (wheels)
3. For attractiveness (wallpaper, windows)

14. Take A Walk; Do A Survey (Entire class)

(A) Take the children for a walk around the school and neighborhood. Find geometric shapes in the houses and buildings in the area. Look for geometric shapes in other things, such as sidewalks, trimmed evergreens, signs, etc.

(B) To impress the notion of geometric shapes:
Have the child make a survey of his home, the school yard, the principal's office, etc., for all the different geometric shapes he can find. Have him find the perimeter of five of the rectangular objects, both by actual measuring and by mathematical computation.

15. Geometric Riddles (Entire class)

Have students develop riddles such as these for their classmates to solve. Have them match the riddle with the answer.

SHAPES : RIDDLES

1. I have 3 sides.	a. Square
2. I have no sides.	b. Triangle
3. I have 4 sides.	c. Sphere
4. I look like a ball	d. Cone
5. I am round but I am flat on one end and pointed on the other end.	e. Circle

16. Measuring Tools for Shapes (Entire class)

Give each student a protractor, a compass and a ruler.

Have each student determine what shapes can be made by using each tool.

Have each student make as many different designs as possible using each tool separately.

Discuss with the entire class the purpose of each tool and its limitations.

17. Sport Shapes (Small groups)

Have a small group of youngsters do a study of the shapes of the tools used in a variety of sports. The group should list the sport, identify the tools or equipment used (e.g. bowling: round ball, wood pins) and the shape of the tools.

As an added activity ask this group to recommend changes in the shapes of the tools of sports and suggest how this might change the game.

18. Words and Shapes (Entire class)

Have the students write in the shape each of the words suggests:

WORD	SHAPE
area	
circumference	
hypotenuse	
volume	
vertex	
radius	
pyramid	
pi	
legs	

19. Shapes and Formulas (Entire class)

Write the following formulas on the blackboard and ask the students to identify shapes with which the formula can be used:

Formula	Shape
$A = \pi \times r^2$	
$A = L \times W$	
$C = \pi \times d$	
$V = l \times w \times h$	

20. Vocabulary Shaping (Entire class)

Have each student find an example or do a sketch of each of the following words before they define it and use it in a sentence: area, base, cube, circle, edge, face, hypotenuse, prism, rectangular prism, square, vertex, polygon.

21. Recognizing Basic Shapes (Entire class)

Provide each child with a blank United States map that has the states outlined. Have pupils make associations between states and the basic geometric shape they most closely resemble. This could be indicated by labeling or superimposing the geometric shape over the outline of the state.

Compare with other youngsters in the class. Discuss any differences in their perceptions.

22. Plane or Solid (Entire class)

Randomly arrange a number of geometric forms, plane and solid, on a table in the room. (Make plane figures of colored construction paper, and solid figures of a material such as styrofoam.) Give students a chance to look at, or perhaps handle the objects. Have students place the figures into categories, giving no specific information or directions. Some possible categories are:

1. Plane figures and solid figures.
2. Similar figures: rectangles of different sizes, triangles of different kinds, circles of various forms, etc.
3. Similar sizes, colors, etc.

Ask students on what basis they have chosen their categories. Select concepts to be taught on the basis of their answers.

23. Make A Shape (Small groups)

Arrange students in groups of six to eight. Have them form geometric shapes by placing themselves in the proper configuration.

Circle   Square   Triangle   Etc.

24. Solid Figures (Small groups)

As youngsters become more aware of the properties of plane figures, they should begin to see some of these same features in solid figures. Have the class form six groups. Have two groups work on the square (plane) and the cube (solid), two groups on the equilaterial triangle (plane) and the pyramid (solid), and two groups on the circle (plane) and the sphere (solid). After thorough examination, have the groups list the similar qualities and the differences of the figures. Have the groups exchange information.

25. Making Models (Entire class)

Have students make wire, pipe cleaner or toothpick models of geometric figures. This enables them to see the "other" sides of the pyramids, cubes, parallelepipeds, etc. Place these models next to the solid shapes for comparison. This will also help children see the figure as being made up by lines, *not* by the area inside of the lines.

26. Geometric Shapes At Home (Entire class)

Have the students compile lists of items found in the home which utilize the geometric shapes studied. Arrange the items according to the rooms they are found in. Which rooms offer the most items? Students can compare their lists with other students in the room. Have students find geometric shapes in their clothing, looking for patterns. Have them design fabrics which could be used for clothing, draperies, etc. This can be done on paper first and then transferred to cloth. Set up a display of the finished samples.

27. Without Shape or Substance (Small groups)

Assign several small groups of youngsters the task of preparing a "presidential report" on what will happen when we deplete our resources of shapes: circles, squares and triangles.

Have each group take one shape and pretend that it will be "all used up" by the year 2000. Ask them to prepare a "presidential report" on what will happen and what will have to be done when the shape is depleted.

28. Shape Puzzle (Entire class)

Duplicate the following puzzles for the students in class:

(A)   S __ __ __ __ __ E   (square)
                              L   (segment)
        __   __   (triangle)
        G
        M   __
        __   I
        __ __
        T

(B)   c   (circle)

```
   ⌒ ╲
  (     )
   ⌣  ╱
```

```
    ∧
   ∠  ⅃
```

(C) Have the students find out how many words related to geometry they can put together starting with

                    A
                    N
                    G
                    L
        S E G M E N T
                          R
                          I
                          A
                          N
                          G
                          L
                          E

(D) Using each of the following words for shapes, have students find out the number of words that can be made from its letters:

Circle	Square	Triangle
ice		

29. Making Jewelry (Entire class)

Make geometric shapes out of papiermache. Paint them with bright colored enamel. Fashion them for necklaces, earrings, bracelets, etc. Students can make this jewelry for themselves, or the class can make them for gifts.

30. Where Do We Find Them? (Entire class)

Investigate geometric forms found in plants, animals and humans. This is rather difficult and youngsters may confuse *symmetrical* with *geometrical*. Good discussion should result.

31. "Mapping" Games (Entire class or small groups)

Have interested students compile lists of sports or games which utilize geometric shapes; examples, baseball (diamond), football (field), hopscotch, etc. Map out the baseball diamond, using brown paper and a magic marker. Show the path which the runners take around the bases with red yarn. With blue yarn show the various paths the ball might take. Do similar "mapping" with the other games.

32. "Mapping" Streets (Entire class or small groups)

Using a large city map, show the geometric pattern of the streets and avenues. Discuss how this helps traffic to move in an orderly fashion. Consider alternatives to this arrangement. What would be the consequences? Could an improvement be made in the present arrangement of the streets?

33. Community Resources (Entire class)

Invite a person who uses geometric figures in his work to

come in and talk to the class. Possible sources are a landscape architect, an industrial engineer, a commercial artist, or an engineer.

34. Pyramids (Entire class and small groups)

Using pipe cleaners or toothpicks and glue, have the students build pyramids. Discuss the ways in which pyramids are built and how the early Egyptians could have constructed them. Examples of pyramids:

Discuss ways in which all pyramids are similar.

35. Mobiles (Entire class)

Have students construct mobiles using geometric shapes. Another concept involved in building a mobile should be stressed, namely, that of *balance*. Display the finished products.

36. Geometric Jigsaw Puzzles (Entire class or small groups)

Using construction paper, cut a variety of puzzles using the geometric shapes that have been studied. Put each puzzle into a separate envelope so as not to mix up the pieces. Have students solve the puzzle by building triangles, squares, rectangles, etc., as designated in the envelopes.

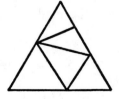 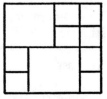 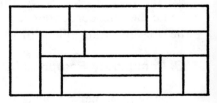

37. What Happened? (Entire class)

Have youngsters experience this activity by using corrugated cardboard, heavy pins and string. Mark each cardboard as illustrated below:

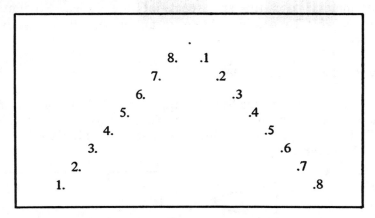

Have students place pins in each dot on the cardboard. Have them take the string and matching the numbers 1 to 1, 2 to 2, etc., and discover that straight lines can create the impression of a curve. Interesting discussion should result. The final product should look like this:

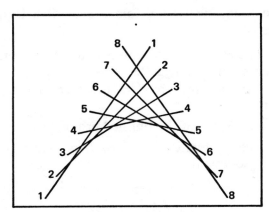

This design can be extended by adding more points and numbers. The sides of the angles do not necessarily have to be of the same length as was the case in the preceding illustration. However, each line or segment used must be divided into equal parts.

38. Line Designs (Entire class)

Have youngsters do line designs by graphing coordinates. This can be done by using circles, squares, triangles, rectangles, etc. There are several excellent publications which delve into both the mathematical and the art aspects of line design. Students are thereby able to combine interests and create things of lasting beauty.

39. Road Signs (Entire class)

Road signs are readily identifiable by their geometric shape. These signs are grouped according to category. Send for a state bulletin where you live to obtain your state's regulations.
Examples:

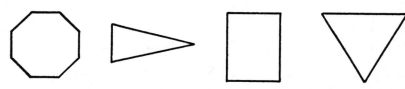

40. Geometric Art (Entire class)

Students can construct geodesic structures by pasting together the following circles, folded according to the following instructions:

1. Cut circles, mark the centers and fold to form three arcs. Colored paper is suggested.
2. Paste or glue the arc sides together to form any desired shape.
3. Make a display of the finished products.
4. Have youngsters explain how they arrived at their particular geodesic form.

4 Measuring Things: 40 Group Activities

This chapter provides forty teaching-learning strategies that encourage students to use and understand measurement as a means of making better and more reliable judgments.

In a sense, this chapter is a natural follow-up of the concepts presented in the preceding chapter on geometric shapes. It demonstrates that measurement is one thing that can be useful in learning about geometric shapes.

This chapter also serves as a supplement to many of the other chapters in this book—numbers in the real world involves measurement; money is a form of measurement; the metric system deals with units of measure.

The activities demonstrate, we believe, that many important applications of arithmentic come about in knowing, understanding and using measurement.

As indicated in other chapters of this book, this chapter is best used by teachers who have determined the needs of students in their classes, who seek strategies that go beyond what one finds in the typical textbook, and who want to actively involve students in what they are learning.

1. Building an Interest Center (Entire class)

Have students bring in items that measure things. Set up a

special table for a display of these items. Examples: measuring cup, clock, ruler, yardstick, weight scale, thermometer, altimeter (a picture will do), speedometer, barometer, tests (to measure achievement), eye chart, audiometer (the school nurse might have one), metronome, calendar, gasoline pump (picture), etc.

2. Why Standardized Measures? (Entire class)

Start a discussion about how man once measured things using different parts of his body (forearm, four fingers, foot), and how inadequate this was. Ask the class: "Why was this method of measurement inadequate?" Discuss the need for the same measurement devices which all people can use.

1. Cut out one-inch cardboard blocks. Paper tape measures may also be used. They are easier to use—just cut them apart.
2. Pass out wooden rulers to all students.
3. Have each student use the one-inch strip and block out sections of the ruler. Ask: "How many times does the strip block out the ruler when you work from end to end?"
4. Place a yardstick on your desk. Have the students take rulers and tell how many fit on the yardstick from end to end.
5. Ask: "What tells us how many inches in a foot?" (Mark on the ruler.)
6. Ask: "Which is longest—inch, yard or foot? Which is smallest?"
7. Ask: "How many inches in a foot? In a yard? How many feet in a yard?"
8. Ask: "What measuring device would I probably use to measure a desk? A bulletin board? A pencil?"

Provide youngsters with a wide variety of experiences with measurement.

3. Linear and Capacity Measurement (Small groups)

Explain the differences between linear (line measurement) and capacity (volume) measurement.

Linear: inch, foot, yard
Capacity: pint, quart, gallon

1. Bring in various kinds and sizes of pots, pans, bottles, cups, etc., and ask selected students to group them into pints, quarts and gallons. Have other students decide whether they agree with this grouping. Discuss. Ask: "What unit of measure is smallest? Largest?"

2. Ask: "If pints are smaller than quarts, how many pints would make a quart?" Have other students each take a pint container and fill it with water. Have them pour the water into the quart container. Ask: "How many filled their quart container?" Try again. Ask: "How many filled their quart containers this time? How many pints in a quart?"

3. Repeat this procedure with different students using quart and gallon containers.

4. Repeat the same procedure using pint, quart and gallon containers. Students should discover that 2 pints equal 1 quart, 4 quarts equal 1 gallon, and 8 pints equal 1 gallon.

4. What's Proper? (Entire class)

Have students select the proper unit of measure for the following:

ITEM	UNIT OF MEASURE
Kool-Aid	(pint, quart, gallon)
Football field	(feet, yard)
Classroom	(feet, yard)
Sugar	(cup, pint)
Height	(inches, feet)
Soup	(pint, quart, gallon)

This list can be extended and should include items brought in by the children.

5. Estimating (Small groups)

Children need practice in estimating and measuring things. Explain what it means to *estimate.*

1. Have students estimate the dimensions of various objects using the following chart.

ITEM	ESTIMATE	ACTUAL	AMT. OVER - UNDER
Blackboard Bowl of water Can of soup Height of chair Etc.			

2. Have groups of youngsters prepare lists. Exchange with other groups.

6. More Measurement (Entire class)

Give each student one of the following items: tennis ball, basketball, ping-pong ball, record (45 rpm), ring, globe, etc. Ask them to measure the object. They will have difficulties. Explain that a different method is required to measure round objects. Ask class for possible solutions.

7. Visual Tricks (Entire class)

Have students estimate which lines in each figure are longer. Then have students measure these lines. In Figure 1, the lines are equal. In Figure 2, the horizontal line is longer. In Figure 3, the horizontal line is longer. (Our eyes find it easier to move across a horizontal line rather than a vertical line; therefore, most people see vertical lines as being longer.)

Figure I   Figure II   Figure III

8. Telling Time (Entire class)

Have youngsters make their own clock faces with movable hands. Have them set the clocks as you direct or match one which you manipulate. Use both Roman and Arabic numerals. Stress the concept of man measuring time and discuss the topic in terms of why it is necessary—for train, plane and bus schedules; appointments; school openings and closings; sports events; etc.

9. Measuring Time (Entire class)

1. Have students investigate how time was determined before clocks or electricity. Examples: sun dials, sand clocks, marked candles, etc.

2. Explore concepts concerning A.M. and P.M. Explain the exact meaning of the initials A.M. (ante meridian) and P.M. (post meridian). The meaning is related to the earth as it revolves around the sun. It can best be remembered for our purposes as A.M. (at morning) from midnight to noon, P.M. (past morning) from noon until midnight.

3. Have students write the times for their activities as follows:

ACTIVITY	ACTIVITY (A.M.-P.M.)
Dinner	6:30 P.M.
Bedtime	
T.V. time	
Breakfast	
Music lesson	
Etc.	

4. Have students write the following with numerals or words:

PROBLEMS	ANSWERS
1. ten-thirty (morning)	10:30 P.M.
2. ten-fifteen (night)	10:15 P.M.
3. 11:20 A.M.	

PROBLEMS	ANSWERS

4. 1:27 P.M.

5.

6.

5. Relate these activities to the time zones in the United States. Have students determine the times in other zones when it is a specific time in their own zone. Ask: "Why does time change as you travel across the country?"

10. Sand Time (Entire class)

Have various sand time measures available. Students can probably assist in bringing in a variety of such timers. Have them estimate time elapsed; then have them use actual clock time and compare results. Interested individuals could be encouraged to do further research regarding the inception and necessity surrounding this method of telling time.

11. Ounces and Pounds (Entire class)

Bring a pound of butter or oleomargarine that has been cut into quarters to class. Ask the students to identify the weight of the package of butter. Ask a student to open the package and estimate the weight of each quarter. Ask: "How many ounces in one quarter pound of butter?" On a scale, have a student weigh a quarter block of the butter. How much does it weigh? If one quarter block of butter weighs 4 ounces, how many ounces will four blocks weigh in ounces? How many ounces to a pound? Ask: "How many ounces in a dozen?" "Can you determine it this way? How?"

Problems.

1. Which weighs more, a pound of butter or a pound of feathers? (It is surprising how many students will say "butter.")

2. Which weighs more, a pound of cheese or 18 ounces of cheese?

3. A company sent Sam one- and two-pound boxes of candy. Sally received some candy from the same company; however, she received three one-pound boxes of candy. Who received more candy?

4. Have youngsters develop problems of their own, using ounces and pounds.

12. Measuring Perimeter (Entire class)

1. Ask the students: "How many feet does a baseball player run when he hits a home run?" (It is 90 feet from home to first base, 90 feet to second, 90 feet to third, and 90 feet more to home plate—a total of 360 feet.)

2. Have them determine how they arrived at their answer (add up all dimensions). Tell them that finding the distance around polygons is called finding the *perimeter.*

3. Have students find the perimeter of polygons such as their desk, books, door, seat, etc.

4. After students find the perimeter of various objects, ask them to write a formula for finding perimeter ($P = 2L + 2W$). Can they develop a "special formula" for finding the perimeter of a square? ($P = 2 (L + W)$)

13. Measuring Circumference (Entire class)

1. Circumference and perimeter mean the distance around an object. Perimeter is used for polygons; circumference for circles or round objects.

2. Have students define a circle.

3. Have students define the parts of a circle:
   a. radius
   b. diameter
   c. chord
   d. arc
   e. tangent to a circle

4. Have students identify the parts of a circle by writing in the proper word in the space provided.

1. (arc) _____
2. (diameter) _____
3. (chord) _____
4. (tangent) _____
5. (radius) _____

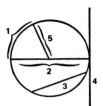

5. Have students confirm the following statement discovered long before the time of the Egyptians: No matter what the size of the circle, the circumference will measure about three times the diameter. Have students confirm this generalization by using a bicycle wheel.

14. Measuring Area (Entire class)

1. Have each student draw a one-foot square on a piece of paper. Ask: "How many inches in each foot?"

2. Have each student block out his paper so that he has 144 inch square blocks.

3. Have students express this quantity as a ratio:

   12 sq. in./1 row $\dfrac{12}{1} = \dfrac{a}{12}$ no. of rows

   Thus, 12 sq. in. in one row, 12 rows in the block equals 12 x 12 or 144 sq. in.

4. Have a student use chalk to mark off a square one yard long and one yard wide. Use the classroom floor. Ask: "How many square feet in this square yard?" Have students use a ruler to mark off three dots in each line of the diagram. Connect these lines. Ask: "How many square blocks in the square yard? What is the size of one block?" Write this problem in equation form.

   $$\frac{3}{1} = \frac{b}{3}$$

5. Put this diagram on the board.

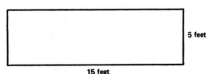

5 feet

15 feet

Ask the students to:

a. Find the perimeter. (40 feet)

b. Find the area. $\dfrac{5}{1} = \dfrac{c}{15} = 75$ sq. feet

c. State why area is always expressed in square feet.

6. Have each student pretend he is going to tile a basement floor that has the following dimensions:

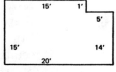

a. After they have explored various possibilities for determining the area, suggest that they block out the floor as follows:

b. Have students find the area of sections A and B

A : $\dfrac{15}{1} = \dfrac{x}{15} = 225$ sq. ft.

B : $\dfrac{14}{1} = \dfrac{x}{5} = 70$ sq. ft.

c. Have students find the total area of the floor. (225 + 70 = 295 sq. ft.)

d. Tell students that they are to tile the floor with asphalt tile which is 9 inches long and 9 inches wide. Each tile will cost 5½ cents. Ask: "How many tiles will we need to cover the basement floor which is diagrammed on the board?" Suggest to students that they change the area of the floor (295 sq. ft.) to inches. (144 x 295 = 42, 480 sq. in.) Ask: "Why use 144 sq. inches instead of 12 inches?"

e. Ask: "How many square inches is each tile? (81 sq. in.) What is the total area in square inches? (42,480) How can we determine the number of tiles we need?" (Divide 42,480 by 81 = 525 tiles, rounded off, no fractions.)

f. If we need approximately 525 tiles, how much will this cost? (525 x .05½ = $28.87½ or $28.88)

g. Tell the students that most catalogs recommend another way to measure for floor tile installation. "Measure width, length of room in inches. Divide by 9 (for 9 x 9 tiles). Multiply together (W x L) to find the number of tiles you need."

h. If we solved the problem as suggested by the catalog, what would be the dimensions of section A and section B of the basement floor? (Solving the problem this way results in needing 533 tiles.) Why does this number differ from the number of tiles we determined in our first process?

15. How Big Is My House? (Entire class)

Have students find the measurements of each room in their home. Have them find the area, perimeter and total square feet of each room.

16. Numbers Tell About (Small groups)

Numbers Tell About
Your height: _____ feet, _____ inches
Your weight: _____ pounds
Your shoe size: _____
Your hat size: _____
Your vision: _____
Your speed: Number of seconds to run 25 feet _____
Your agility: Number of seconds to deal 52 cards _____
Your jumping ability: Number of feet you can jump _____

Have each student complete as much of this card as possible by himself, giving directions when necessary. Let him measure, investigate and assist others as he works.

17. Ancient Measures (Entire class)

In ancient Egypt, the human body served as the basis of measurement. Have students complete the following chart.

Using Body Measurement		
Parts of body	Unit of measure	Findings
Forearm	1 cubit	
Foot	1 foot	
Four fingers	a palm—1/7 of a cubit	
Finger	a digit—1/4 of a palm	

18. Measuring in Palms (Entire class)

Have students develop a chart similar to the one below and, using the width of four fingers, measure the objects to the nearest unit of each. Then have the students compare their answers to actual measurements in feet and inches.

Object	Length in palms—feet—inches
1. Mathematics book	
2. Desk	
3. Spelling book	
4. A sheet of paper	
5. Pencil	

19. Which Is More? (Small groups—Teams)

Have students make up problems such as the following:

WHICH IS MORE?

Circle the right answer.

3 quarts or 7 pints

2 feet or 25 inches

20 days or 3 weeks

20 minutes or 90 seconds

Have them quiz other group or team members to determine if they understand equivalency measures.

20. Equivalencies (Entire group)

Have students prepare cards (about 5″ x 8″) on which they record various liquid measurements (3 pints, 2 quarts, 4 cups, and so on.) Several cards may be placed on the chalk tray. Ask a child to pick the card naming the greatest liquid measurement. Then have the child tell why the choice is correct. Have the pupil demonstrate his choice by actually measuring out his decision using water, sand or other such materials.

21. Guess How Heavy? (Small groups)

Fill ice cream cartons (pint size) with varying amounts of sand and seal carefully with cellophane or other tape. Have students try to arrange them according to weight by holding each one. Weigh the cartons on a scale to check the accuracy of their estimates.

22. The Match Game (Entire class)

Duplicate the following activity. Have the pupils match the measures named in the first column with the measures named in the second column.

1. foot	a. 2 pints
2. 1 yard	b. 4 quarts
3. 1 pint	c. 12 inches
4. 1 quart	d. 8 quarts
5. 1 gallon	e. 6 feet
6. 2 feet	f. 2 cups
7. 2 yards	g. 3 feet
8. 2 gallons	h. 24 inches

Items can be added or deleted depending upon the level of knowledge of the students.

23. The Unusual (Entire class)

Have students prepare and present unusual measurements such as a: ten-penny nail, cord of wood, 100-watt bulb, number 3 pencil, number 3 can, pieces of eight, British thermal unit, 16-pound paper, "two bits" of money, etc.

24. Scale Drawing (Entire class or small groups)

Have students make a "Secret Treasure" or "Lost Mine" map. Students should indicate the scale and the legend. Ask them to write four questions that can be answered by using the map. Have students exchange maps with their classmates.

25. Meter Reading (Entire class or small groups)

Have pupils check the type of meters they have in their homes: gas, water, electric, etc. Have them draw diagrams that represent the readings. Have them check the readings at periodic intervals. The readings can be compared to the bills received by the family.

A field trip to various utilities in the community could be helpful in further explaining how the companies "measure" the consumption of their particular product.

26. Shadow Sticks (Entire class or small groups)

Have some students make a "shadow stick." Have others observe as he/she marks the length of a shadow on the stick at specified times of the day. Continue this over at least a three-day period. Students should ultimately be able to estimate the time of day using the "shadow stick." If possible, try to get a sundial and have students compare their findings with sticks to the readings on the sundial, and then to the actual time.

27. Strange Instruments (Entire class)

Have students find out about one of these instruments and what they measure and report to the class.

Micrometer

Protractor
Transit
Sextant
Caliper

28. Balance Scale (Entire class)

Have students make a balance scale by using a coat hanger, two strings of equal length and two tie pins. Use objects of known weight to determine the weight of other items. To determine the accuracy of the home-made balance scale, have students weigh the objects on a regular scale. To add to this activity have the students: (1) estimate the weight of the object; (2) weigh the object on their balance scale; (3) weigh the object on a regular scale. Compare results.

29. On The Playground (Entire class)

There are numerous activities that youngsters are engaged in during the physical education period. Many of these activities lend themselves to measurement. Have students measure distances for physical sports such as the baseball throw, the high jump, the long jump, the shot put, the standing long jump, etc. Have them keep records of their own progress.

30. Boom! Boom! Boom! (Entire class)

Discuss how the heart rate is measured and how you can take your own heart rate by measuring your pulse beat. Each student can chart his own heart and keep a record of its beat at rest and prior to and following certain designated activities. Have students compare their charts with others. Discuss the possible reasons for variance between individuals. This activity also lends itself very well to graphing.

31. Inhale—Exhale! (Entire class)

Follow a procedure similar to the previous activity, substituting breath rate. Be careful to watch the time period (one minute), and have it remain constant.

32. Fun in the Kitchen (Small groups)

There are a number of cookbooks available which are written for youngsters. Most of these books contain recipes for cookies, candies, salads, etc., which do not require cooking or baking. Have each group select a recipe which they will make. Use standard measuring cups and spoons and impress on the youngsters the need and reason for accurate measurement of the ingredients. Halve and double the recipes. Groups can eat their own projects, share their goodies with other groups or have a bake sale. Home-made treats such as this also make tasty gifts for such occasions as Christmas, Easter, Mother's Day, Father's Day, etc.

33. Measuring Common Kitchen Staples (Small groups)

Have items such as salt, flour, sugar, noodles, oatmeal, farina, coffee, etc., available for the youngsters to measure. Have them determine whether the amounts in cups are equal to the amounts in ounces. Ask questions such as:

1. Which items are equal and which are not?
2. What accounts for similarities and differences?
3. Why do recipes call for some things to be measured by spoons, some by cups and some by ounces or pounds?
4. What other kinds of measurement are necessary in cooking?

34. A Cup is Not Always a Cup (Entire class)

The cup manufactured to contain beverages does not represent the cup with which we have been dealing. All pupils may use a standard measuring cup at home and compare it with other beverage containers called "cups" to see how much variation there is. Have them report findings to the class. If possible, have them bring in samples of the cups they used and demonstrate the differences.

35. Reporting Weather (Entire class)

All weather reports relate conditions by some number representation. Have youngsters watch several different weather reports on television. Have them list all the ways that weather is measured: air temperature, water temperature, wind velocity, barometric pressure, rain or snow fall amounts, humidity, high and low tide (in areas where it is appropriate), etc.

36. Investigation (Entire class or small groups)

Investigate the different instruments used to make the measurements listed in the previous activity.

Investigate and report how this information is helpful and related to man's everyday activities.

37. Make Your Own (Small groups)

Have each group make different weather measuring instruments—thermometers, barometers, etc. Directions for making these instruments can be found in science activity books. Have each group record and share their findings, and compare them to professional weather reports.

38. Time and Temperature (Entire class or small groups)

Have the pupils read and record the indoor and the outdoor temperature readings for several days. Then have pupils tell at what time of day the thermometer had the highest reading outside and inside, and when the thermometer had the lowest reading outside and inside. Is there a pattern? What factors could account for similar or dissimilar readings? Are there other kinds of "temperature" readings?

39. What Does "Mean" Mean? (Entire class)

Since temperature, rainfall, snowfall, etc., are also reported in terms of the mean (for the month, the year, the area), it is important for youngsters to have some understanding of the meaning of this term.

As you know, the *mean* of a series of numbers is the "average" of those numbers, and is computed by adding all of the numbers and dividing by the number of numbers used.

Demonstrate the concept of mean or average by using this device. Use strips of "tickets" and present strips containing 15, 13, 12, 8 and 7 "tickets." Work with pupils in removing some tickets from strips containing 15, 13 and 12 and attaching them to strips containing 8 and 7. Thus, five equivalent strips of 11 "tickets" each are formed. The mean or average is 11. Now, illustrate this procedure on the blackboard: add 15, 13, 12, 8 and 7, and divide by the number of numbers (5); thus, $55 \div 5 = 11$. Eleven is the mean or average.

40. Fahrenheit/Centigrade (Entire class)

Make models of the Fahrenheit and centigrade scales out of posterboard. Use thin movable strips of colored paper for the columns of colored liquid. Have pupils use the models to show a given reading on each scale; then they can make conversions from Fahrenheit to centigrade and from centigrade to Fahrenheit. (For more metric activities, see Chapter Nine.)

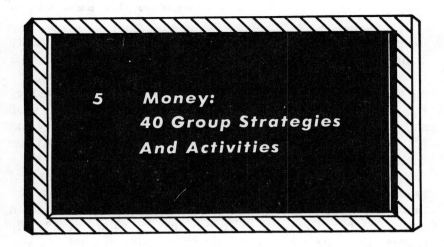

**5   Money:
40 Group Strategies
And Activities**

Money is a math motivator. Using money in math classes not only helps youngsters to understand fractions, decimals, whole numbers and computation, but the use of the activities in this chapter will highlight these understandings:

(a) Prior to the use of money, *barter* was the only form of trade.

(b) Money was invented because of inter-country trading.

(c) Metals (gold, silver) became a widely used medium of exchange and sacks of coins were used in buying things.

(d) Paper money replaced many coins.

(e) Each government decides its own money unit.

(f) People can buy and sell things without the use of money by using checks, credit cards, etc.

Many people handle some money almost every day, but few stop to ask where it came from or why it is valued so highly.

What does money do for you? Students should discuss the answers to this question before trying out the activities in this chapter.

First, money serves as a *medium of exchange*. Suppose that you are eager to buy a bicycle, and that you must earn enough money to pay for it. You may do this, perhaps, by mowing lawns for people in your neighborhood. You would have some difficulty in finding a person who has a bicycle to sell and who at the same time would be willing to hire you to mow his lawn. Therefore, you mow lawns for many different people who pay you with money for your services. With this money you can go to a bicycle shop and make your purchase. The merchant accepts your money and you get your bicycle. Money has performed a service. It has enabled you to *exchange your labor for something you wanted.*

Second, money serves as a *yardstick of value.* This means that money may be used to measure and compare the values of various things. You may value your services in mowing a lawn at 35¢ an hour. The bicycle you wish to buy may be valued at $25. By learning the price which is asked for all kinds of products, you may measure their value because you know the meaning of a dollar.

Third, money is also a *storehouse of value.* A farmer might not be able to hold his crops for a very long time because they are perishable, but the results of his labor can be conveniently preserved for his future use if he is paid with money.

Fourth, money serves as a *standard for future payments.* Suppose that the dealer from whom you purchase your bicycle lets you have the bicycle after you make a down payment of $5. You then agree to pay the rest of the cost at a later date. You will not pay in eggs, baseballs or roller skates. You both recognize the value of money as a form in which later payments can be made.

In addition, youngsters will be interested in the activities of this chapter which demonstrate that every country has its own units of money. For example, the United States uses the dollar, England uses the pound sterling and Japan uses the yen. These basic units are broken down into smaller units of money.

(a) The United States dollar equals 100 cents.

(b) The English pound equals 20 shillings.

(c) The Japanese yen equals 100 sen.

A person can exchange money for the money of any country according to certain rates.

(a) One pound sterling is worth about $2.00.

(b) $1.00 is worth about 358 yen.

(c) Usually such rates are set by the central banks of a country.

The value of a country's currency may change depending on economic and political conditions in the country and in the world.

Since each government decides its own units of money, teachers should review money in their own country. Key concepts and key words are underlined for emphasis.

In the United States it is the *dollar*. Each government also specifies what currency is *legal tender*. Legal tender is money that can be used to pay debts. All United States currency is legal tender.

Paper money has *value* only because some government guarantees it. In the United States a bill worth one dollar is the same size as one worth $10,000, but people accept the value printed on each bill because the federal government guarantees that it is worth that amount.

Each government selects a *standard*—usually either gold or silver—on which the value of its money is based. The gold or silver owned by a government makes it possible for that government to guarantee the value of the paper money it prints. The money system of the United States is based on a gold standard. The government has about $20 billion in gold stored at Fort Knox, Kentucky.

Money in the United States is controlled by the Treasury of the United States and by banks of the Federal Reserve System. Coins are made at federal mints in Denver and Philadelphia. All paper money is made at the Bureau of Engraving and Printing in Washington, D.C.

1. "Moneyology" Study of Money (Project groups)

Arrange the class into groups of four or five students to select one of the following books or other references to prepare reports, bulletin boards, ads, reviews, etc., on the content of each book.

1. Alcorn, John. *Money Round the World.* New York: Harcourt, Brace, World, Inc., 1963.

2. Buehr, Walter. *Treasure, The Story of Money and Its Safeguarding.* New York: G.P. Putnam's Sons, 1955.

3. Elkin, Benjamin. *The True Book of Money.* Chicago: Childrens Press, 1960.

4. Foster, Constance. *The Story of Money.* New York: Nedill, McBride, Co., 1962.

5. Russel, Solveig. *From Barter to Gold.* Chicago: Rand McNally Co., 1961.

6. Wilcox, Louise. *What Is Money?* Austin, Texas: Steck Co., 1959.

2. Money Talk (Class Discussion)

Discuss with your students answers to the following questions recording key concepts, statements and opinions on the blackboard for further use.

1. What does money do for you?
2. What does it mean to "barter"? Do you do it now?
3. Why is gold a medium of exchange?
4. How can people buy and sell things without the use of money?
5. What are some of the advantages and disadvantages of credit cards?
6. What are the advantages and disadvantages of using checks?

3. Money Poetry (Small groups)

Arrange the class into small groups of three or four students. Ask them to try math poetry in two ways. The first way is to try to rewrite rhymes and limericks using money words as follows:

Jack and Jill went up the hill,
To fetch a paper dollar.
Jack came down with half the bill,
Jill had half a dollar.

The second way is to have each group write their own poems about money. These should be shared in some way—on the bulletin board, on tape, in the class poetry book, etc.

4. Play Money (Entire class)

Use "play money" to strengthen concepts regarding the names and values of the various denominations. Example: A Monopoly game will provide bills of 500, 100, 50, 20, 10, 5 and 1. Cardboard discs make good coins.

   A. Teach students to read these numbers
   B. Have students determine the value of the money by providing items for them to "buy." Example: A book has a price tag of $2. One student sells it to another. He receives a $5 bill. How much does he give back to the other student?
   C. Have students study various money combinations for a certain piece of currency. For example:

$1	$5	$10
2 half dollars		
4 quarters		
10 dimes		
20 nickels		
100 pennies		
1 half dollar and		
20 pennies, etc.		

The concept here is that money involves grouping by fives and tens. For example, a nickel is equal in value to five pennies; a dime to two nickels; a quarter to five nickels, etc.

5. Interviewing the Money People (Special interest groups)

Prepare a list of people that deal with money—bankers, brokers, coin collectors, accountants, etc.

Have each group select one person from the list you prepared. Arrange to have each group conduct a 10 to 15 minute tape recorded interview. Have each group prepare questions prior to the interview.

Plan a radio program format of fifteen minutes each day for playing the tapes each group made. Have each group design their own program format for the "broadcast."

6. Introducing Decimals (Entire class)

Using money concepts provides an excellent way of introducing students to decimals. First, put these numbers on the board:

$1.00 $ .75 $1.50 $ .66 $ .07

Ask students to identify the value of each number and say it aloud. Also ask the following questions:

(a) "How are these numbers different?" (They have different values)

(b) "What does this sign ($) mean?"

(c) "Why is seven cents written $ .07?"

(d) "What is this called (.)?"

(e) "What is it used for?"

7. Writing Money Numbers (Entire class)

Have students practice writing "money numbers." Write the following as numbers:

(a) Seven dollars and fifty cents

(b) Twenty-two cents

(c) Twelve dollars and seven cents

(d) Sixteen dollars and fifty cents

(e) Eighty-eight cents

(f) Etc.

Now write these numbers as words:

(a) $101
(b) $25.52
(c) $130.33
(d) $1200.01
(e) $99.22

8. In the Beginning . . . (Entire class)

The introduction of this chapter provided some background on the origin and use of money. Use that content and the references in activity one to discuss with the class answers to the following questions:

(a) How did primitive man trade?
(b) Why did primitive man trade?
(c) What did primitive man use for money?
(d) Who do we trade? Person to person? Government to government?
(e) Why are metals such as gold and silver used for money?
(f) What is "legal tender"?

9. Money Problems (Remedial Groups)

Children experiencing difficulty with computation, problem solving or decimals and fractions may benefit from completing money problems. Ask other members of the class to assist you by preparing money problems from newspapers and magazines that emphasize a particular math skill such as the addition of decimals. Each side prepares two or three problems, gives them to you for review or rewriting, and then has the remedial group try to complete the problems. The aides do the correcting and assist remedial group students in analyzing their errors.

10. Posters! Money Around the World (Project groups)

Have each project group (three or four students) select two or three countries and design posters that explain that country's money system. Place these posters in the school corridors for other students to see.

11. Foreign Money—The Real Thing (Entire class)

Ask students to bring in foreign money for display on the "money table." Each student is to write out a 3 x 5 card telling about the money brought in, where it came from, how much it is in U.S. money, etc.

12. Making Cents! (Entire class)

Using pictures of coins or real money, have the students complete the following:

What is the total value of

(1) 2 dimes and 1 penny

(2) 2 quarters and 1 penny

(3) 3 nickels and 1 half dollar

(4) Name the total values in cents

pennies	1		9	3	4		6	1	3	4	8	2		5	3	2
nickels	3	3	1	7	3	4			4	7	1	3	2	6	7	
quarters	3	1	4		1	3	2	6	2	1	3	1	3	1		9
half-dollars	1	2		2	4	1	1	2	1	1	2	2	1		1	1
total value																
in cents	A	B	C	D	E	F	G	H	I	J	K	L	M	N	O	P

Example A = 141 ¢

13. How to Order (Entire class)

Set up a mail order house. Use various merchandise catalogs and have children order materials from these catalogs. All procedures stated in the catalogs should be followed. Youngsters receiving the orders should check them for accuracy. Order blanks can be developed by the class and mimeographed in quantity.

14. Math—Maps—Money! (Entire class)

In order to have students realize that different countries use different kinds of currency, prepare an outline map of several countries, including the United States. Have students place on the map the capital of the country, the currency used, some pictures of the country, etc. Help youngsters with the pronunciation of words that represent the currency of foreign countries.

15. Food Funds (Entire class)

Set up an International Cafeteria. The school lunch program may be used for this purpose. Have each student select a country. Then have the students make coins from cardboard that represent the currency used in that country. Also, find out what foods are the most popular in that country. Have students act out buying their lunches or snacks using the foreign currency to pay for it. Posters may be made on the foods and the cost in the currency of the country under study.

16. How Much? (Entire class)

Provide students with some conversion problems as follows:
1. In France, 10 francs equals 3 cents in U.S. money. What is the value of 20 francs? 30 francs?
2. In Belgium 50 francs has the same value as $1 in the U.S. What is the value of 100 francs? 500 francs?
3. In Spain, 25 centimos equals 1/2 cent in U.S. money. One peseta equals 2 1/2 cents. What is the value of 5 pesetas? 10 pesetas? 50 pesetas?

(The dictionary is a good source for additional information on monetary units and denominations. Because of the constant variation in exchange value however, the daily newspaper might provide a more accurate table.)

17. Travel Math (Project groups)

Have each project group gather maps, flyers, travel folders, newspaper and magazine ads and articles and prepare an imaginary-trip scrapbook to a foreign country. Have each group determine all of their costs for the trip—itemized—in terms of the currency of that country and in U.S. currency.

18. Converter Bank (Project groups)

Have a project group of students (three or four) set up a "Converter Bank." All other students select a country, prepare paper money and cardboard coins to represent the currency used in the selected country, and then give it to the bank. Distribute "play money" to all but the bank tellers. Have each student determine the type and amount of currency he should receive from the bank teller when he goes to the bank to convert his American play money into the currency of the country he selected.

19. Foreign Money (Entire class)

Have students list under each country the name of the currency used in that country, for example:

Name of Country	Currency Used
Great Britain	sixpence, shillings, pounds
Ireland	" " "
France	francs
Switzerland	centimes, francs
Italy	lire
Holland	cents, guilders
Germany	pfennig, marks
Austria	groschen, schillings
Norway, Sweden, Denmark	ore, kroner
Portugal	centavos, escudos
Spain	centimos, pesetas
Greece	leptas, drachmas
Israel	prutas, pounds

20. Currency Equivalents (Entire class)

Have students complete the following chart giving approximate equivalencies:

U.S.	Great Britain	France	Germany	Italy	Turkey
.25	2 shillings	80 francs	1 mark	150 lire	1 lira
.50	4 "	195 "	2 "	300 "	1 ½"
1.00	7 "	350 "	4 "	625 "	3 "
5.00	2 pds. 16 shillings	1800 "	21 "	33,000 "	14 "
Etc.					

21. Math Folk Fair (Project groups)

Have students set up a folk fair or a bazaar. Each group will use the money that represents a particular country, and students should try to dress like the people of that country. Each booth can "sell" pictures or articles representing the country, but these are sold only in that country's currency. Music and dances of each country should be part of the folk fair.

22. Money Problems (Entire class)

Have each student prepare five money problems on a 3 x 5 card. Put all these cards in a box. For homework or free time, have each student select five cards and do the problems. The student who prepared the original problems should check the other students work for the correct process and answer.

23. Research (Independent study—Extra credit)

Have volunteers research such questions as:

(a) Are there countries that use something other than money to obtain goods?

(b) What is the International Check System?

(c) How do banks handle foreign money?

(d) When countries do business with one another, is money exchanged between them?

(e) What are Federal Reserve Banks?

(f) How does a credit card system work?

24. Money Word Bank (Entire class)

Give each student twenty-five slips of newsprint cut out to resemble the size of a dollar bill.

A box with a slot in its top, appropriately decorated can serve as a money bank.

Each student is to deposit one of their slips when they have identified four money-selected words—two words on each side of the slip.

Use the bank to make withdrawals, using words for vocabulary building, spelling lessons, etc.

25. Money Filmstrips (Special interest groups)

Purchase a filmstrip kit (Prima Education Products, Irvington-On-Hudson, N.Y. 10533). Have special interest groups make a filmstrip on an area of interest such as: "The Making of a Penny," "Machines That Take Money—Use It—Count It," "Money and the Decimal System."

Each group should also prepare a tape to go along with each filmstrip and present their creations to the class.

26. Problem Solving (Entire class)

Hand out a sheet of math problems to each student that is somewhat different from the typical math-money problems that they do. Here are two examples:

Problem 1: If you have a penny the first day of the month and double your savings each day (1 penny the first day; 2 pennies the second day, 4 pennies the third day, etc.), how much will you have at the end of a 30-day month?

Problem 2: Assume you have won a million dollars. How many days would it take for you to spend it if you spent one thousand dollars per day?

27. Projects (Groups)

Here is a list of projects that groups of students can complete.

1. Investigate how money is made.
2. Find out all you can about U.S. mints.
3. Prepare a report on the U.S. Treasury—how it got started and what it does.
4. Investigate some of the great money robberies—prepare posters for the class.
5. Investigate cliches and sayings about money and prepare posters illustrating each one you can find. Examples: "A penny saved is a penny earned;" "Money is the root of all evil."

28. Word Cents Game (Team learning)

Arrange the class into teams of two or three students. Tell them that they are going to play the "Word Cents Game." You will write a money word on the board and then give them a specific amount of time to find as many words as they can using the letters of that word. For example, you could write on the board: "NICKEL—5 minutes." Each team tries to get the largest number of words using the letters in "nickel" in a five-minute session.

29. Tic Tac Mo (Team learning)

This game is designed for two players. The usual tic-tac-toe board design is drawn. Each player calls the focus of the game before it starts. For example, one player might say "symbols." The game is then played using money symbols. It is best played if one player uses a red pencil and the other a regular pencil or pen. The first one to fill in three symbols in a row—horizontally, vertically or diagonally—wins. The loser then calls the next game. Example: one half as much. Each player gives the other player a price—one-half of fifty cents. The other player writes the answer or, if he doesn't know it, he writes in a question mark.

Three question marks in a row lose; three answers win.

30. Money and Sport Salaries (Special interest groups)

Have each special interest group (three or four students) select a sport—baseball, basketball, football, hockey, soccer, tennis, golf.

Each group is to find out the names and salaries of the ten highest paid players.

When all the information is gathered, the groups should come together, prepare a chart and explain their findings to the class.

Charts should include: (1) listing of players and salaries from highest to lowest; (2) comparison of salaries for each sport—which sports pay top athletes the best, etc.

Students may also wish to investigate the average salaries of players in each sport, and make appropriate comparisons.

31. Checking Costs (Entire class)

Have students collect cash register tapes from purchases at supermarket and other stores. They are to be placed in a box. Students are to select a certain number of tapes and add the cost of the items (mentally or with a hand calculator) to verify the totals on the tapes (addition of decimals.)

Subtraction problems can be designed by writing the amount of money the purchaser may have given the clerk, and calculating the amount of money refunded to the purchaser.

Example: The cost for a list of items on one tape totalled—$42.58. On the bottom of the tape the teacher (or student) writes the amount of money given the clerk; in this case, it is two twenty-dollar bills and one five-dollar bill. Question: How much does the clerk return to the purchaser?

32. Money Graphs (Entire class)

Each student prepares a table on the amount of money he

expects to spend and actually needs over a one-week period. After the results have been tabulated in table form, have them do a line graph of their expenditures. Have each student write an interpretation of what his/her graph shows.

Table Example:

Day	Spending–Estimated	Spending–Actual
M	$ .23	$ .20
T	.70	.75
W	.30	.20
T	.50	.48
F	.66	.80
S	.29	.21
S	.41	.32

Graph Example:

```
S    $ .80
P      .70
E      .60
N      .50
D      .40
I      .30
N      .20
G      .10
      . 0
       ─────────────────────────────
        M   T   W   T   F   S   S
```

33. Estimation—How Much Does It Cost? (Team learning)

Students should be given a variety of opportunities to learn the skill of estimation. Teams of students can compete between themselves and other teams in estimating such things as:

1. The cost of five different brands of cereal.
2. The amount of interest paid to purchase a $3,000 car for 3 years at 12% per year.
3. The cost of tickets to a play for four people at $5.25 per ticket.

4. The number of one-dollar bills in circulation in the U.S.

5. The amount of money a wage earner will earn over a 40-year period at $600 per month.

Scorecards can be designed for keeping and recording how much.

34. There's Money in Eating Out (Special interest group)

Have the class estimate the number of restaurants in your community. To determine the accuracy of this estimate, use the Yellow Pages in the phone book. This, too, is an estimate, since some restaurants may not be listed. Have the class try to categorize the restaurants in their community—those that are national chains, those that are attached to hotels, those that are local, etc. Have each of the special interest groups investigate each category and determine the average cost of a meal for one person and for a family of four. Each group should obtain the menu and discuss prices, services, etc. Students can discuss why national chain restaurants are so popular, the advantage and disadvantages of eating at different kinds of restaurants, and the like.

35. The Money-Makers (Team learning)

There is an old saying, "If you want to make money, you have to have money." Have learning teams (two students) investigate views to this cliche, and the answer to this question: "How does money make more money?" Each team should research one of the following positions to complete this assignment: stockbroker, businessman, bondsman, real estate broker, banker, economist, savings and loan company officer, mutual fund officer, etc.

Answers can be compared and presented to the class, and generalizations made by the entire class.

36. FBI vs SPG (Special interest groups)

Have special interest groups (three or four students) investigate money matters such as:

1. How credit cards work.

2. The when, where, why and how of borrowing money.

3. How to finance a car.

4. Money and gambling.

5. Transportation: the prices go up.

Each group should initially prepare a list of questions that they and their classmates would like answered. Interviews should be arranged, resource material collected, and methods of presenting information to the class determined.

37. Who Makes What? (Team learning)

Students are usually interested in the salaries people get in various occupations. Teams of students can be assigned four or five occupations and chart their data as follows:

Occupation	Preparation	Yearly Salary	Fringe Benefits
Teacher			
Lawyer			
Plumber			
Salesman			
Etc.			

38. Bills! Bills! What Do They Mean? (Entire class)

Have students collect examples of bills people receive. Each student with the help of the teacher can learn to understand the information in each bill. For example, each student can bring in one copy of a water bill, telephone bill or electricity bill. The bill can be checked for accuracy, payment information, penalties and the like.

39. Money Baseball (Entire class)

In order to provide students practice in solving money

problems, prepare (with student help) about 75 cards with money problems on them: about 20 with money addition problems as "singles," 20 subtraction problems for "doubles," 20 division problems for "triples," and 15 multiplication problem "home-runs."

Divide the class into two teams. One player on each team is the pitcher and, when the other team is "at bat," he/she reads the problem randomly from the "pitcher's box." If the "batter" gives the right answer, he/she goes to the base designated by the problem (set up areas in the class for the bases.) The "batter" giving a wrong answer or no answer is "out." Three outs complete an inning. Each game is seven innings; the team with the most runs wins.

40. Paying for Education (Special interest group)

Have a group of three or four students find out about financing education in their community.

Have the students arrange an interview with the school business manager, if there is one, and/or the superintendent. Also have the students interview one or more board members.

Students should prepare some of their questions prior to the interview. The following questions can serve as guidelines:

1. Who pays for our education?
2. How do the citizens pay?
3. When do they pay?
4. Does the board have a budget calendar?
5. How much does it cost to educate the youngsters in this community?
6. How much money comes from local resources? State? Federal?
7. What percent of the money is spent on salaries? Materials? Maintenance? Extra-curricular activities (sports, dances, etc.)?
8. What is the importance of the average daily attendance?
9. How many citizens attend the board's budget hearings?

This special interest group should prepare an oral report to the class using the appropriate visual aids. A written report to the class and parents would also be of value.

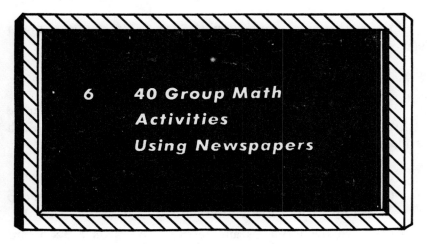

6   **40 Group Math Activities Using Newspapers**

In an earlier book, *Creative Units for the Elementary School Teacher* (Parker Publishing Company Inc., 1969), the authors devoted one chapter to the use of newspapers in each subject matter area.

In one of his college classes, the author asked teachers to examine the math skills and concepts in a popular elementary math series. The problem was to determine how many of these math skills and concepts might be taught with a medium other than a math textbook. To everyone's surprise, almost all of the math content for grades one through eight could be taught using daily newspapers. This is not to suggest that math textbooks should be replaced with newspapers; rather, it provides evidence that daily newspapers contain material that teachers can use to supplement the textbook.

But why should a teacher use newspapers in math classes? First, our experience documents the fact that newspapers are filled with math concepts, skills and problems that are useful in the classroom. Second, newspapers contain math concepts, skills and problems that are practical, realistic and up to date. Third, newspapers are a great motivator; students like to use newspapers, and if students are interested and motivated they become more productive—they learn the math you are trying to teach them. Fourth, newspaper content can be used by the teacher to individualize math instruction, to help youngsters explore math processes and problems on their own.

Here, then, are group activities using newspapers that should make learning math fun, meaningful and productive.

1. Math Problems (Small groups)

Have five or six small groups (two or three students) prepare about five math problems using content from newspapers. Each group should:

(a) Cut out the content from the newspaper;
(b) Write out the math problems on a sheet of paper and clip it to the newspaper cutout;
(c) Solve the problems and record answers on a 3 x 5 card and place it in an answer box;
(d) Place all problems in a problem-solving box.

Each group then selects four or five problems from the box (their own may not be used), solves them, and checks the answers with those in the "answer box."

2. Booklets (Project groups)

Each project group should prepare a small booklet on the math content that appears in several newspapers for one week.

One group can prepare a booklet on "Math in the News;" another on "Ads Add Up" (math in ads); another on "Small and Large Numbers in Newspapers;" and another on "Symbols," i.e., $ (dollar sign), % (percent sign), 49¢ (cents sign), etc.

3. Math Words (Small groups)

Give each group of students (three or four students) two or three daily newspapers. Tell them that when you say "go," they will have five minutes to find as many math words as possible. At the end of the five minutes, one student from each group will write their words on the board. The group that wins directs the spelling lessons on these words next week. Each group will be expected to spell and define the words the entire class found in newspapers. Among such words will be inflation, recession, loans, stock, sale, price, creditors, savings, discount, twins, double, recount, bargain, money, measure, etc.

4. Planning a Party (SmallGroup)

Have each group plan a Friday or Saturday party for ten girls and ten boys. Provide each group with play money. To make it more interesting, one group gets twenty dollars, another fifteen, and so on, until one group receives only five dollars for their party.

Each group is to cut out ads of what they will spend and use at their party and paste them on construction paper; they are not to exceed the amount of money provided. Each group then prepares a schedule of their three hour party; i.e., 7:00, introductions; 7:10-8:00, games; 8:00, food and drinks (to be identified); etc.

The entire class should be encouraged to discuss the similarities and differences in party plans between those who had little to spend and those who had much to spend. The teacher might ask: "Does the amount of money you spent relate to the success of your party?"

5. Doing Your Thing (Special interest groups)

As we have stated, certain groups of students may wish to explore or investigate other activities after completing some of the activities in this chapter. Special interest groups may wish to investigate the differences, costs and printing procedures for several kinds of ads that appear in a newspaper—national ads, local ads, classified ads.

Other special interest groups may wish to investigate occupations in the newspaper business, and salary and benefits for each occupation.

6. Surveys and Graphs (Project groups)

Arrange the class into four project groups of six or seven students each. Assign three groups a sample to survey regarding newspaper reading habits: one group can sample teachers' newspaper reading habits; another, parents; the third, other students in the school. The fourth project group should report on national and local surveys concerning the newspaper reading habits of the American public.

Each group should prepare a survey sheet that includes some of the following: time spent reading a newspaper; content read regularly; etc. Each group should then prepare graphs on the data collected. The teacher should help each group utilize a variety of graphs—line graphs, pie graphs, bar graphs.

7. Sets (Self-help groups)

Have one group of students help individuals or groups in your classroom who are having difficulty with any math process, but in this activity, the focus is the concept of "sets." The helping group can cut out pictures of all kinds (food, merchandise, etc.) that can be scrambled together and then sorted into sets by the individual student or groups of students experiencing difficulty in understanding this concept. Have each one tell why their groupings can be called sets.

8. Subsets (Self-help groups)

Once the students in the self-help group have mastered the concept of sets, ask the helping group to introduce the concept of subsets, using a pattern similar to the following:

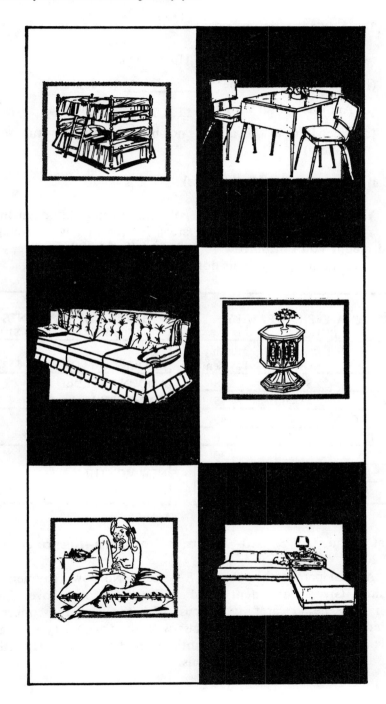

The helping group can ask:

(a) The set is _____ (furniture).

(b) One subset would be _____ (beds).

(c) Another subset would be _____ (tables).

(d) What item in this ad does not belong in the furniture set? (Pillow)

9. Can You Afford It? (Entire class)

You can substantially reduce your current monthly payments by paying off old debts. If you are a homeowner with average good credit, you can borrow $3,000, $4,000, $5,000 or more, yet keep your monthly payments down to what you can afford.

HERE'S A TYPICAL FAMILY BUDGET		
Account	Owed	Monthly Payments
LOAN	$1,100	$68
AUTO LOAN	1,400	75
HOME REPAIR LOAN	750	45
CHARGE CARDS	550	40
STORES	250	30
ODD BILLS	450	50
TOTAL	$4,500	$308

HERE'S HOW PAYMENTS OF $308 WERE CUT TO $105	
AMOUNT OF LOAN	$5,000
AMOUNT NEEDED TO PAY BILLS	4,500
EXTRA CASH FOR YOU	500
NEW MONTHLY PAYMENT	$105

Total payment of $8,820—7 years, 84 payments—finance charge, $3,820.

Annual percentage rate is 18 percent. No down payment is required. Give each student an ad similar to the one above. Have them read the ad carefully. Discuss with the class the concepts behind such an ad. Assist the class with the vocabulary such as: annual percentage, finance, substantially, credit, account. Have the class answer the following questions:

(a) According to the ad, how much does the "typical family" owe? ($4,500)

(b) What are its monthly payments ($308)

(c) How long would it take to pay off the $4,500 at $308 per month? (about 14.8 months)

(d) You borrow $5,000 to pay your debts and agree to pay $105 per month for 7 years—84 payments. How much do you pay the company? ($8,820) How much more did you pay above the $5,000 loan? How much did the company make on your loan?

(e) What are the advantages and disadvantages of borrowing money in this way?

10. Ordinal Numbers (Entire class)

Teach ordinal concepts using this ad. Pass out the ad to the class and read the following directions to the class (note: you are also teaching listening skills):

(a) Does everyone have their crayons and a pen or pencil?

(b) Listen to my directions and let's find out if you can follow me as we go along. Ready?

(c) Color the *first* circle above the lever red.

(d) In the *second* circle, write a 2. Next to the number 2, print out the number *two.*

(e) Color the *third* circle green; the *fourth* circle yellow; the *fifth* circle orange; the *sixth* circle blue.

(f) Put a 7 in the *seventh* circle; put black dots in circle *eight.*

(g) Put the first letter of your first name in the *ninth* circle.

(h) Put the first letter of your last name in the *tenth* circle.

11. Weather (Team learning)

Weather charts provide teachers the opportunity to inter-relate geography, science and math. Teachers and student groups can use weather maps and data to teach map reading skills, math skills and use of symbols. Teachers and student groups can design geography lessons based on the weather map; science lessons can include understandings of fronts (cold, warm, stationary), pressure areas (high, low) and weather patterns; math lessons can include activities such as the one that follows. Have one team of students prepare lessons or activities for other teams to complete using weather charts and questions as shown in the following examples:

Tomorrow's Weather Map

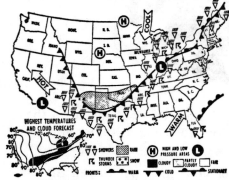

National Weather Service Data Adapted by The Journal

(a) How many hours and minutes between sunrise and sunset?

(b) How many hours and minutes between moonrise and moonset?

(c) According to your computations, was the moon out as long as the sun?

(d) What is the normal high for the day? The normal low? The range or difference?

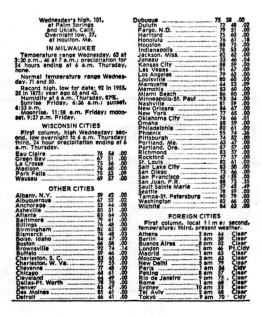

(e) Compute the temperature ranges for each city in Wisconsin. Of the six cities listed, which one had the largest temperature range? How does this range compare with the range in Milwaukee?

(f) What city had the greatest amount of precipitation? The least? Did it rain in Wisconsin? Where? How much?

(g) Which foreign cities had a higher temperature than that in Milwaukee? Lower?

12. Question Asking (Entire class)

Provide each student with the ad on hardwood chairs. Have each student read the ad and answer the following questions (See Chart 12):

(a) You are decorating your home or apartment. You need six ladderback chairs without arms for your dining room. How much would it cost?

(b) Your recreation room would look great with five swivel stools around the table. How much would this cost you?

(c) Suppose you wanted to pay cash for one of each of the chairs (counting the chairs with and without arms) in the ad. How much cash would you bring? Would it be enough since you also need to pay a Wisconsin sales tax of 4 percent? How much more would you need? What is the total cost?

HARDWOOD SPECIAL 4 DAYS Thurs., Fri. Sat., Sun.

Captain Chair $21⁹⁵

MATE CHAIR $16⁹⁵

Desk Chair $11.95

Swivel Stool $29.95

Duxbury Rocker $24.95

Duxbury Chair $21.95

Ladderback 24.95
With arms 29.95

Windsor 24.95
With arms 29.95

STORE HOURS:
Mon., Thurs., Fri., 9 to 9;
Tues., Wed., Sat., 9 to 5:30
Oklahoma and Appleton Ave. Stores
Sunday, Noon to 5

USE OUR
MIRACLE WIPE ON FINISH
Each coat wipes on with a cloth, no brush, no fuss, no
experience needed. And it really works. All of today's
popular colors.

De Luxe Captain 24.95

De Luxe Mate 19.95

13. Baseball Math (Entire class)

Give each student a baseball standings chart similar to the one pictured here:

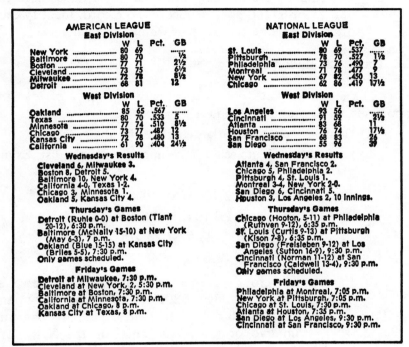

Have each student:

(a) Compute the percentage for each team in the American League East and National League West;

(b) Place all American and National League teams in order based on the teams' won-lost records. Which team is first? Last?

(c) Arrange the teams in the American League West and National League East in alphabetical order based on teams over .500 and teams under .500.

(d) Compute the total runs scored in American League teams on Wednesday; do the same for the National League. Which league scored more runs? How many more?

(e) List the teams that will start Thursday's games after 6:00 p.m.; after 9:00 p.m. (Milwaukee time). How many teams are playing afternoon games?

(f) Determine what pitchers for Thursday's games have the best records; the poorest record; no record. Identify each pitcher by name and by their winning percentage.

14. The Stock Market (Small group)

The stock market quotations provide a variety of teaching strategies; a few are suggested here.

(a) Explain the stock market chart to the students.

(b) Have the students select a company from the list. Example: Nabisco

   Ask: (1) What does 2.30 mean? (dividend)

   (2) What does PE 10 mean?

   (3) How much is 23 5/8? 23 1/8?

   (4) What does +3/8 mean?

(c) Have small groups (three or four students) serve as brokers. Give each student $200 of play money. Set up the class so that the brokers sell shares. Students can buy stock from two or three companies on the New York Stock Exchange. Students should select their companies; pay the price for the number of shares they will buy; keep a chart (on graph paper) of the progress of their stock on Mondays, Wednesdays and Fridays; buy and sell when they wish.

(d) Have each group select three stocks from the stock market page and answer the following questions:

   (1) Which stocks were most active for the day?

   (2) Are the stocks you selected *common* or *preferred*?

   (3) How much would 50, 100 and 200 shares of each stock cost you without the broker's fee?

   (4) Which of the stocks that you selected pay dividends? How much?

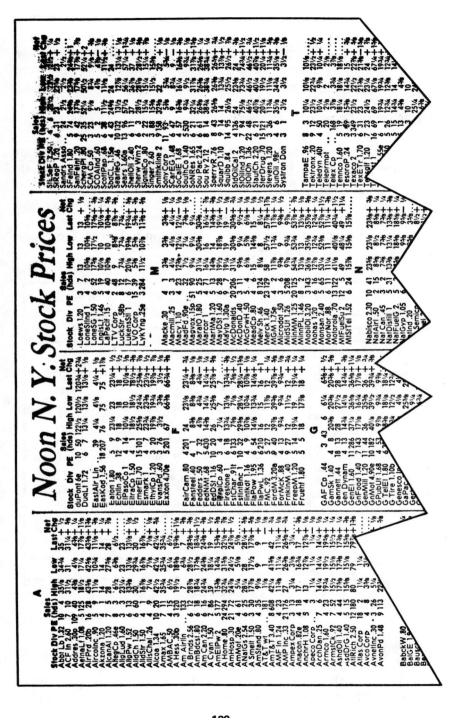

(5) Which of the stocks that you selected had the greatest change—"high" and "low"—for the year? How much was the change?

15. Made to Order (Entire class)

We spend a considerable amount of time filling out forms of one kind or another. In this activity you should ask the students to begin a collection of order forms that appear in the newspaper. When you have enough to give two to each student, design activities similar to the one shown here.

You and your family plan to buy season tickets to the opera. Complete the following form:

FLORENTINE OPERA COMPANY   TICKET ORDER FORM
NAME_____
ADDRESS_____
CITY_____ STATE_____ ZIP_____ PHONE_____

AIDA	THURS., OCT. 10	SAT., OCT. 12
L'ELISIR D'AMORE	THURS., NOV. 21	SAT., NOV. 23
MANON LESCAUT	THURS., MARCH 13	SAT., MARCH 15
TALES OF HOFFMANN	THURS., MAY 1	SAT., MAY 3

QUANTITY_____

ORCH. A-V ..... @ $11.50   LOGE A-E ...... @ $11.50   LOGE K-N ...... @ $ 8.50
ORCH. W-Z ..... @ $10.50   LOGE F-J ...... @ $10.00   BALCONY (Thurs. @ $ 6.50 only)

SIDE LOGE SOLD OUT

BEVERLY SILLS—LUCIA DILAMMERMOOR—SPECIAL GALA ☐ THURSDAY, JAN 23 ☐ SATURDAY, JAN 25
QUANTITY_____

		CHECK OR MONEY
ORCH.–SIDE LOGE		ORDER ENCLOSED $_____
LOGE A-E	$25.00 each	
	($13.50 TAX DEDUCTIBLE)	CHARGE TO MY
LOGE F-J	$20.00 each	MASTERCHARGE #_____
	($10.00 TAX DEDUCTIBLE)	
		BANKAMERICARD #_____
LOGE K-N	$15.00 each	
	($ 6.50 TAX DEDUCTIBLE)	GIMBELS #_____
BALCONY	$10.00 each	
	($ 3.50 TAX DEDUCTIBLE)	SEARS #_____

PLEASE MAKE CHECKS PAYABLE AND MAIL TO: PERFORMING ARTS CENTER BOX OFFICE,
929 NORTH WATER STREET, MILWAUKEE, WISCONSIN 53202.
PLEASE ENCLOSE A STAMPED, SELF ADDRESSED ENVELOPE WITH YOUR ORDER

16. Math Problems (Small groups)

Have small groups (two or three students) prepare math problems based upon a variety of ads and math content appearing in newspapers. They can then share their problems with other groups in the class. Here is an example.

Read this ad and then complete the questions that follow:

That's as much as you'll have to pay
for a 3-minute, direct-dial long distance
call to anywhere in the 48 continental states—if you call
between 5 PM Friday and 8 AM Monday.

Weekend long distance rates are even lower if you place your
call between 8 AM Saturday and 5 PM Sunday.

It's just another way you save when you place your long distance
calls without operator assistance during off-peak hours.

Have a good trip.

**SAMPLE WEEKEND DIRECT-DIAL LONG DISTANCE RATES.
EFFECTIVE 5 PM FRIDAY TO 8 AM MONDAY.**

FROM WISCONSIN TO:	3 Minutes	5 Minutes	10 Minutes
ST. LOUIS	60¢ or less	$1.00 or less	$2.00 or less
NEW YORK	70¢ or less	$1.10 or less	$2.10 or less
MIAMI	75¢ or less	$1.25 or less	$2.50 or less
SAN FRANCISCO	75¢ or less	$1.25 or less	$2.50 or less

Federal excise and state taxes not included. Dial direct rates apply on all calls (excluding Alaska) completed from a residence or office phone without operator assistance. They also apply on calls placed with an operator to a residence or office phone where direct dialing facilities are not available. Dial direct rates do not apply to person-to-person, coin, hotel-guest, credit card, or collect calls, or to calls charged to another number.

(a) What would it cost your group to call all of the cities listed in the ad if you talked to each party for ten minutes?

(b) What are the state and federal taxes on long distance phone calls?

(c) Add the state and federal taxes to your phone charges in problem (a). What is the total cost?

17. Area and Perimeter (Entire class)

After explaining the concepts of area and perimeter, have one or two youngsters cut out of the newspaper floor plans of houses so that each youngster has one or two similar to the one that follows.

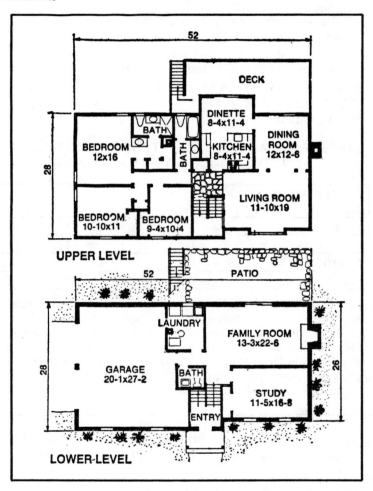

Prepare a ditto sheet that includes the following questions to be answered by each student.

(a) What is the perimeter of the entire house?

(b) How many floors in this house?

(c) What is the area of the upper level?

(d) What is the area of the lower level?

(e) What is the area of the entire house?

(f) What is the area of the garage? Is it a one- or two-car garage?

(g) Estimate the perimeter of the patio.

18. Ad Shopping (Project groups)

Assign four or five project groups to try comparison shopping, using ads from newspapers. Assign one group foods, another medicines and vitamins, another automobiles, etc. Students should prepare charts, booklets on brand names, the price of a specific item in four or five different ads, etc.

19. Good News—Bad News (Small groups)

Ask the class whether, in their opinion, newspapers print more good news than bad news. Record the vote on the board.

Give each small group (four or five students) two copies of their daily newspaper. Have each group select a section of these newspapers, or assign specific pages. Students in each group can use a ruler to measure the column inches of good news and bad news for each section and/or pages they were assigned. Each group should record their results on the blackboard or make a transparency of their findings. Do the findings support the majority vote of amount of good news vs. bad news?

20. Scan and Skim Game (Entire class)

Give each youngster a daily newspaper. Have eacn one turn to the front page and follow these directions:

(a) In two minutes, circle all the math words and numbers you can find;

then have the ten students with the most words or numbers circled turn to the sports page and follow these directions:

(b) In one minute, circle all the math words and numbers you can find;

then have the five students with the most words and numbers circled turn to the classified ad page and follow these directions:

(c) In thirty seconds, circle all the math words and numbers you can find.

Repeat the game using any page in the paper you wish.

21. Quickies (Entire class)

Here are three activities youngsters can do when they say they have nothing to do.

(a) Have each student assume he or she receives a gift of $5 to buy school supplies. Using newspaper ads, have students prepare an itemized list of what they would purchase.

(b) Ask each student to select one ad and rewrite it, converting all numbers to a base other than ten.

(c) Have each student find and cut out newspaper items relating to volume—gallon, pint, quart, etc.

22. Preparing a Classified Ad (Entire class)

Review the classified ad section with the class, noting the directions for submitting a classified ad. Ask each student to prepare a classified ad for something they would like to sell. They are to follow the directions, compute the cost of the ad if it is to run for one, four or six days.

23. Classified Ads (Small groups)

Arrange the class into small groups of about four or five students to carry out one or more of the following activities:

One group can compare the classified ads for houses to rent, houses for sale, apartments to rent, and condominiums for sale.

Another group can compute the cost of all multiple ads for sports cars, sailboats, etc.

A third group might chart and graph the number of classified ads that appear in their daily newspaper from Monday to Friday. What issue, other than the weekend, carries the most classified ads, etc.?

24. Vital Statistics (Special interest groups)

Special interest groups of three or four students may be organized to record, chart and graph some or all of the vital statistics that appear in their daily newspaper for one or more weeks. For example, each group may be assigned one of the following. When completed, the groups bring their data together for the class to analyze:

(a) the average age and range of deaths;
(b) the average age and range of men and women who are being married;
(c) the average age and range of men and women getting divorces;
(d) the number of marriages vs. the number of divorces;
(e) the number of births;
(f) the differences between births and deaths.

25. Newspaper-Shapes Bulletin Board (Special interest group)

Have one group volunteer to prepare a bulletin board display on geometric shapes (circles, triangles, etc.) that they find in their daily newspapers over a three- or four-day period.

26. Area (Entire class)

Cut out ads like this one and have students complete the questions which follow.

$1⁵⁰ Per Square Foot
Gets you . . .

**6047 North Flint Rd.
Glendale**

8,800 Sq. Ft. of finished custom office and warehouse space:
Immediate occupancy.

- Private front entrance
- Private rear entrance
- Complete ___om facilities
- Privat___
- 18___

(a) What is the cost for occupying 8,800 sq. ft. at the price stated in the ad?

(b) At 8,800 square feet, what would be the approximate size of the office?

27. Recipes and Fractions (Entire class)

Have one or two youngsters cut out enough recipes from newspapers so that each student has one. Then have each student study the recipe. Ask them to rewrite the recipe so that it will serve (a) their family; (b) the class; (c) only three people.

28. Math Concepts (Small groups)

Arrange the class into small groups of about three or four students. Each day for one week, spend about twenty minutes having each group clip materials from newspapers and make posters on:

(a) concepts of size (biggest, smallest, tall, short, trial size, king size, etc.);

(b) concepts of time (today, tomorrow, yesterday, two-week trip, etc.);

(c) concepts of quantity (all, more, some, less, etc.);

(d) concepts of value (bargain, true weight, 100 percent orlon, etc.);

(e) concepts of money (10 percent off, $3.98, three for a dollar, etc.).

29. Newspaper Structure (Small groups)

Arrange the class into small groups of three or four students. Give each group a different newspaper—one group should have the local newspaper; other groups should have large or small daily newspapers; another group should have weekly or international newspapers. Have each group count and measure column inches and note those newspapers that provide for pictures, headlines, news stories, special feature stories, puzzles, sports, etc. Each group is to summarize the data and make a presentation to the entire class.

30. Are You Open? (Project groups)

Ask a project group of five or six students to list, from the ads in their local newspaper, the number of large and small department stores that advertise in one week. In addition, have this project group compute the hours these stores are open. What conclusions can they make relative to large and small department stores? Why?

31. Charts and Graphs (Project group)

Provide a project group of five or six students with a variety of newspapers. Have them go through these papers and cut out all the charts and graphs they can find and the articles that go with the charts and graphs. Have the group identify the kinds of graphs and charts used, why they are used and whether or not they are helpful for interpreting the content of the article and so on.

32. Metrics (Entire class)

Have students collect articles that discuss and explain the metric system. Have each student write a one or two sentence summary of each article that they found and read. Ask each student to select a grocery ad and convert the items listed to the metric system, e.g. sweet peas—8 ½ ounces equals 241 grams, tomato juice—46 fluid ounces equals 1.36 liters, etc.

33. Saving (Entire class)

Find ads similar to the following and study the ad with the class. Ask the class to define words or terms such as annual rate, annual yield, minimum, early withdrawals, accumulated, etc.

Put your money to work today in one or more of these savings accounts.

Annual Rate	Savings Plan	Minimum	Annual Yield
5.25%	Regular Passbook	$10	5.39%
5.75%	90 Day Golden Passbook	$10	6.00%*
6.50%	1-Year Certificate	$1000	6.81%*
6.75%	2½-Year Certificate	$1000	7.08%*
7.50%	4-Year Certificate	$1000	7.90%*
7.75%	6-Year Certificate	$1000	8.17%

*Note: Annual yield shown is based on 1 year's accumulated interest. Substantial interest penalty is required on early withdrawals.

Provide each youngster with one or two math problems based on the ad. For example, suppose you used the "1-year certificate" savings plan and deposited $2000. One year later you want to withdraw your money. How much would you withdraw?

34. Weekend Guests (Entire class)

Using the daily newspaper, have each student plan entertainment and figure costs for two friends who will be staying with them over the weekend, using a chart similar to the one that follows:

SATURDAY

Activity	Place	Cost
Breakfast (9:00)	————	————
To Do (9:30-12:00)	————	————
(a)	————	————
(b)	————	————
Lunch (12:00-1:00)	————	————
To Do (1:00-6:00)	————	————
Dinner (6:00-7:00)	————	————
To Do (7:00-11:00)	————	————

35. Sports—What Are the Percentages (Entire class)

There are many student activities that can be used with the sports page. For example, have each student select a team; compute the percentage of number of games won and lost; compute the percent of games won in a particular week; determine, if it is a basketball team, the percentage of shots attempted and made, the percentage of free turns attempted and made, etc.

36. Planning a Trip (Small groups)

Arrange the class into small groups of three or four students. Have each group use newspaper articles and ads to plan a local, national and worldwide trip, depending on their selection. Each group should determine individual and group costs, time, etc.

37. Find a Job (Special interest groups)

Have special interest groups use the classified ad section to identify the kinds of jobs being advertised, the qualifications, the number (example—one paper had 15 classified ads for waitresses), etc.

Each group should prepare a chart on one occupation appearing in the classified ads for one week.
For example: JOB: Salesmen-women

Number	Kind	Qualification	Training	Salary	Other

38. Decimals (Remedial groups)

Ask several students to help you prepare material—worksheets, real problems, etc., for a specific group of students having problems with decimals. Have these students find in their newspaper how decimals are used and prepare lessons for the remedial group. You might suggest that they look at the sports pages, ads (dollars-cents), stock market reports, weather reports, etc., as they prepare their materials. Have the remedial group complete the sheets and then consult the student who designed it for the answers.

39. Numbers in the News (Entire class)

Encourage each student to clip out articles that serve as examples of the use of numbers in our daily life and limit the activity only to news articles. Have each youngster underline the numbers used in news articles and record as follows:

Date	Number of Articles	Number of Numbers	List
Monday	3	15	$3 billion
			$67,440,000
			etc.

40. Your Time? (Entire class)

Using the television section in their daily newspaper, have each student clip out this section, circle the programs they watch each day for a week (Monday through Sunday); compute the amount of time that they watch television each day; compare this time to the number of hours they are awake, in school, and playing outside. Discuss the results and implications of this activity with the entire class.

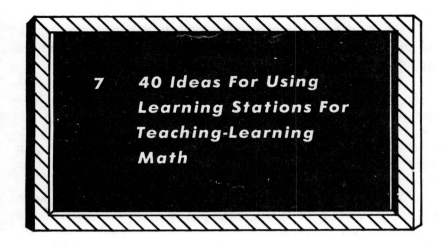

7 40 Ideas For Using Learning Stations For Teaching-Learning Math

No single teaching strategy has captured the interest of creative teachers as much as learning centers and learning stations.

For our purposes a learning center is an area in the classroom where children can initiate and pursue individual and group projects. It embraces those skills we identified in the preface of this book—namely, responsibility, accomplishment, leadership and problem solving.

A learning center provides teachers the opportunity to create small groups and individual instructional strategies; to observe students in these activities; to design interesting and stimulating activities so that students become motivated and self-directed.

The same can be said for learning stations except that we consider learning stations to be less comprehensive than a center, but not of lesser importance, because stations have been employed by teachers as a way of individualizing instruction.

One teacher calls learning centers and stations "the extra teacher in your classroom." We wish we could transmit the excitement and ideas teachers express when they design their classrooms in centers and stations. Kim Marshall was able to do this in her article "The Learning Station Way" (*Learning*, Sept. 1973, pp. 34-39). She says "learning stations also opened the door to one of the most delightful sets of personal relationships I ever had, thus creating an atmosphere in which both the kids and I grew enormously."

Many of the teachers we work with usually have one center for each subject—math, science, social studies—and several learning stations around the room for student use.

A math center, for example, might be in one corner of the room on a large table set under a bulletin board. The center might contain math books, pamphlets, filmstrips, records, charts, commercial math games, teacher-made math games, student-made math games, play money, reference books, scissors, glue, poster paper, filmstrip viewer, puzzles—almost anything that pertains to math teaching and learning.

Your task as a teacher is to determine what results you want from this math center. What group and individual social skills should the students learn? What math skills should be learned? Bob Eberle designed an excellent checklist for establishing learning centers ("A Learning Center Is What You Make It" in *Instructor*, Jan. 1975, p. 82).

Learning stations are very effective for individualizing instructions. They are very useful for learning math skills. Teachers usually establish several stations around the classroom. Some teachers, with the help of the more able students, design five to ten stations every two weeks. These stations can be tacked up on bulletin boards around the room or they can be placed at desks around the perimeter of the class—one station to each desk. Students can complete learning stations at their own pace or guidelines can be established by the teacher.

Remember that one of our major points, for the purposes of the activities that follow, is that a learning center is primarily for group activities (small groups, team learning, etc.) and a learning station is for individual activity. We guarantee that the use of centers and stations will allow you more time to hold conferences and to talk with each of your students.

The first twenty activities would be used best with learning centers, while activities 21 to 40 are designed to be used for learning stations.

1. Survey Basic Facts

Have a small group of students determine the extent to which their classmates know basic facts in multiplication and division.

(They will need your help in designing a test or they can use your knowledge of who doesn't know those basic facts.) Have the group design practice cards and games to help other students learn multiplication and division facts.

2. Self-Help Groups

Have a group of students who are having difficulty with some of the basic facts in math use the learning center to design strategies that will help them learn basic math skills. For example, one group might design charts such as the following:

Multiplication & Division Chart					
	2	3	4	5	9
2	4	6	8	10	18
3	6	9	12	15	27
4	8	12	16	20	36
5	10	15	20	25	45

3. Advertising Math

Using the resources in the math center, have an independent study group (about five to seven students) prepare *advertisements* that are designed to encourage other students in their class to read and do problems in a specific chapter of the math texts.

4. Make a Filmstrip

Have two or three special interest groups select a math area—decimals, fractions, multiplication, sets, etc. After they have selected their area, the students outline the basic categories involved. For example, among categories in the decimal area the students might list:

(a) meaning of the word "decimal" and the purpose.

(b) changing decimals to common fractions.

(c) changing common fractions to decimals.

(d) adding and subtracting decimal fractions.

(e) division with decimal fractions.

(f) multiplying decimal fractions.

(g) percentages

The group should determine the basic operating principle/concepts/content for each category and insure that all in the group understand these. Once this has been accomplished the teacher should encourage each group to make a filmstrip for each category. The filmstrip should be designed so that it will help other students learn the concepts, principles and content. Teachers can purchase filmstrip kits for use in the math center. The kits come with directions and suggestions for use.

5. Poster Contest

One of the most enjoyable teaching strategies is a math poster contest. We have tried it with teachers. The ideas, creativeness and art work is often amazing both to us and to the teachers involved. It's also a good way to keep those bulletin boards attractive and pertinent.

Announce that the math center will have, during the next week, materials and supplies for your monthly poster contest. You can change the theme of the contest each month. You can also use this strategy to find out if student understands basic concepts of content you have been teaching. Here are some monthly suggestions for the first half of the year.

September: Math: Why Study It?

October: What's the Angle?

November: The Name of the Game. (Math vocabulary)

December: A Life Without Numbers.

January: Fractions Fracture Me.

February: Math and Other Subjects. (How math is used in science, health, social skills, etc.)

March: Math in Our Lives. (A collage of how we use numbers, etc.)

We suggest the awarding of prizes. These need not be

expensive—something silly, at times, is best. However, everyone should get a prize and all posters should be displayed.

6. Comic Strip Math

Have ten learning groups (two or three students) cut out newspaper comic strips (particularly Sunday comics) and rewrite them using math content problems, etc. This is not as easy as it sounds, but students have a lot of fun with it.

7. Cartoon Capers

Have ten learning groups (two or three students) collect cartoons from newspapers and magazines and rewrite the dialogue or captions using some math content or principle. For example, you might ask one or more team learning groups to select two cartoons and rewrite dialogue or captions to include the Venn diagram or Roman numerals, or the distributive property. These can be displayed around the math center and interpreted, and sometimes questioned by other students.

8. Puzzles

Special interest groups should be encouraged to use the materials in the center to make puzzles on math context currently being studied by the class. Not only does this help the student, but it is an additional aid to the teacher.

9. Learning Aids

Have special interest groups ask other teachers in the school what teaching aids would be of value to them. The groups can make these for the teachers; for example, ring-toss games, tagboard clocks, counting boards, etc.

10. Make a Test

Have each special interest group study a filmstrip or a chapter from one of the math books, and design a test that will help you and your students assess how much they know about the content.

We have found this a particularly good way for determining the value of a filmstrip in learning math content. For example, a special interest group studies a filmstrip on multiplication. They then design a test. The teacher can use the test before and after showing the filmstrip. This is also an excellent strategy to use with remedial groups.

11. Math Bibliography

Have a special interest group assist the school librarian by undertaking a study of the math trade books available in the school and local library. After this has been completed, provide this group with publishers' catalogs so students can compare what the libraries have to what is available. Have this group prepare the "don't have" for the librarian. Also have them investigate how the librarian selected math books.

12. Math and Music

Have small groups of students design a math center or learning station that will enable other students to gain appreciation and understanding of how mathematics is related to music. They can include content and activities related to measure, beat, notes, time and the like.

13. Make a Book

Special interest groups could make small math books for youngsters in other grades. For example, one group could make a math book on fractions, another on whole numbers, a third on decimals, etc. Each group should be encouraged to study the style and format of a book, the title, author(s), the cover, table of contents, chapters, etc. Each book should have a catchy title such as *How to Fracture Fractions*, or *Dealing with Decimals*. The construction of the book can be left to each group and then they should plan how it is to be duplicated or if single copies of the book are to be made.

14. Math Fair

Using the math center as the major planning area, have the entire class plan a math fair that would be of interest to other students in the school. Discuss with the class how the fair should be organized, what groups should be responsible for specific tasks, what will be displayed at the fair, how will they know the fair was a success or not, and when and where should the fair be held. For example, there could be several booths emphasizing numbers, ring toss, bean bag throw, dice throw, spin the wheel, etc.

15. Theme Week

Set up one section of the center each week so that it focuses on a math theme with projects for students to do. For example, one week can be Percentage Week; another might be Measurement Week. Using this idea would provide the students with a variety of activities for completion each day of the week. Here is an example for Percentage Week:

Monday: Everyone goes to the gym; each student tries to put the basketball in the basket; each student must record the number of baskets made and number missed, and compute the percentages of each.

Tuesday: Separate the class into about five groups.

Group 1: Watches the news (1/2 hour) program on television and determines the percentage of total time given to advertising.

Group 2: Listens to radio programs (1/2 hour) and determines the percentage of total time given to advertising.

Group 3: Select two or three pages (other than the front page) from their local newspaper and determine the percent of column inches given to advertising for each page.

Group 4: Does the same as group 3 using magazines—determine percent of full-page ads, half-page ads, etc.

Group 5: Survey a group of parents to determine what percentage of the mail for a two-day period is advertising.

Wednesday: Everyone in class determines the percentage of time they have spent yesterday—at home, in school, sleeping, watching TV, playing, working, etc.

Thursday: Give everyone a copy of the sports page from several issues of a variety of newspapers. Each student is to make two percentage problems based on sports page content. Each student trades off the two problems with a friend who answers the problem.

Friday: Using the groups from Tuesday's lesson, have each group select at least one of the following to compute:

(a) percentage of blue-eyed and brown-eyed students in class.

(b) percentage of girls and boys.

(c) percentage over a certain age; under a certain age.

(d) percentage over a certain height; under a certain height.

(e) percentage with blonde hair; brown hair; black hair; etc.

(f) percentage with birth dates in summer; fall; spring.

16. Math Tapes

One way to help students in your remedial groups—or students having difficulties with certain math concepts or processes—is to ask peer-teaching groups to prepare cassette tapes with pencil and paper activities. This can be useful to the other students. For example, in one classroom a group of students were having difficulty understanding the difference between area and perimeter and the processes of finding each. Two groups were asked by the teacher to help her to prepare a cassette tape and paper and pencil activities to go along with the tape on each topic—one group prepared the tape and activities for fellow students on the concept and process of finding the area of something; the other group did the same for perimeter. The teacher told us that each group did an excellent job; that the tapes and activities were useful; that it is an excellent way to individualize instruction, and that she is saving the tapes to use during the next school year.

17. Math Words Collection

Set up a math vocabulary board, (or use butcher paper) in math center. For one week, have the entire class find any word that they can that relates to mathematics. They are to tack or glue their words to the board or paper. They will be surprised at the number of words they collect. Use these words for language arts activities, spelling, writing, reading, etc.

18. Math Wordplay

This idea comes from Mr. Brandel, a syndicated cartoonist, who does a cartoon called "Wordplay." In the center have the students select one or two words from the collection board (activity 17) and do a visual for that word. It's more fun if the words are selected at random. Here is an example:

```
┌─────────────────────┐
│                     │
│   A                 │
│                     │
│   N                 │
│                     │
│   G  L  E           │
│                     │
│                     │
│                     │
└─────────────────────┘
```

19. Commercial Games

Have small groups (two or three) bring in one commercial game and explain to the class the math implications, concepts and processes involved in playing the game. Leave the games in the center for one or two weeks so that students can play them.

20. Math in Occupations

Have a box in the math center filled with cards on different occupations—plumber, banker, reporter, dry cleaner, electrician, politician, teacher, taxicab driver, musician, etc. Each student is to select at least two cards from the box and investigate via books, interviews, etc., how math is used in that occupation. Then each student must present a summary of his/her findings to the class in some way other than telling the class the findings—posters, tapes, filmstrips, etc.

The next twenty activities are designed as learning stations. Learning stations in this chapter, as we have stated previously, are areas where students complete a certain activity. The following stations can be posted around the room and students can complete them within the prescribed time limits you set. Each station can be mounted on oaktag or poster paper. A station may also be designed with a single desk, with materials on that desk for students to complete. Students can record their answers on a learning station score card, and drop it in their folder. You or a teacher aide (or other students) can correct it and return it to the student.

Please note that the learning stations that follow are not always complete; that is, we are suggesting an activity and expect each teacher to design a complete learning station based on our suggestions or sample.

21. Learning Station 1: What's My Pattern

Complete each pattern by placing the figure, number or letter in the blank on your scorecard. (Each student takes a 3 x 5 index card from the learning station prints his/her name and answers to learning station.)

(A)	O	□	O	□	____	____	____
(B)	?	!	!	?	____	____	____
(C)	0	2	4	6	____	____	____
(D)	1	3	5	7	____	____	____
(E)	1	1	2	3	____	____	____
(F)	0	5	0	10	____	____	____

ANSWER CARD–LEARNING STATION 1
(A)
(B)
(C)
(D)
(E)
(F)

22. Learning Station 2: Private

Number Detective.
1. Decode this message; record on your answer card.

23-8-1-20	9-19	25-15-21-18	14-1-13-5?
(What	is	your	name?)

Code:

A = 1,   B = 2,   C = 3, ...   Z = 26

2. Do these activities:

   If A = 2, and B = 4, what number would you assign to C, D, E, etc.?

3. Write your school's name in number code.

4. Have each class member make up a code of his own and ask others to try to decode the message.

5. Develop your own number code of their own and send me a message on your answer card.

6. Develop a Number Detective Code using Roman numerals instead of Arabic numerals. (Attach it to your answer card.)

ANSWER CARD LEARNING STATION 2
(1)
(2)
(3)
(4)
(5)

23. Learning Station 3: Making A Graph

	SAT.	SUN.	MON.	TUES.
9:00-10:00				
10:00-11:00				
11:00-12:00				
12:00- 1:00				
1:00- 2:00				
2:00- 3:00				
3:00- 4:00				
4:00- 5:00				
5:00- 6:00				
6:00- 7:00				
7:00- 8:00				
8:00- 9:00				
9:00-10:00				
10:00-11:00				
11:00-12:00				

Directions:

(1) Make a graph on a sheet of paper like the one shown.

(2) Color in the squares that show the times you were watching television.

(3) Make a graph like this one on some topic such as your friends favorite kinds of ice cream or favorite TV show. Attach this graph to the card before putting it in your learning station file.

24. Learning Station 4: Know Your Fractions.

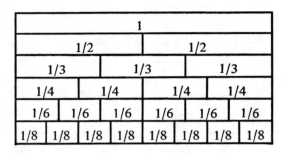

Directions: Using the chart, tell whether the fractions in each of the problems below is less than (<) or more than (>) the fractions that follow it. Record your answers on your answer card by writing (<) or (>) only.

(1)   1/4 1/2   (2)   3/8 3/4   (3)   1/2 2/6   (4) 1/4 1/8
(5)   1/3 1/2   (6)   2/6 3/8   (7)   5/8 4/6   (8) 1/2 2/3
(9)   5/6 3/4   (10) 3/4 1/2   (11) 2/3 3/4   (12)3/4 4/6

25. Learning Station 5: Sets and Subsets

Directions: Answer the following on your answer card for this station.

1. Name some sets in our classroom.
2. Name some subsets from the sets you have named.
3. Diagram to show the relation between sets and subsets.

Example:

A = (all the members of the class)

B = (the girls)

C = (the boys)

---

4. Make a diagram of your family and see how many sets and subsets you can find. (Put this on the back of your answer card.)

Example:

A =   (Miller family)

B =   (Mr. and Mrs. Miller)

C =   (Sally Miller)

D =   (Bill Miller)

E =   (Male members of the Miller family)

F =   (Female members of the Miller family)

---

26. Learning Station 6: What Base Are You On?

+	0	1	2	3
0				
1				
2				
3				

X	0	1	2	3
0				
1				
2				
3				

Directions:

(1) Copy these charts on a piece of paper.

(2) What base are these addition and multiplication tables?

(3) Complete the table.

(4) Construct your own table for base 6—work it out—attach with papers and place in your learning station table.

27. Learning Station 7: Your Deal

Below you will find a deck of cards.

Directions (1) Find a partner. (2) Deal out an equal number of cards to you and your partner. (3) Each of you is to call a math process (addition, subtraction, division, multiplication) and then play a card. The other gives the answer.

For example: One says addition and his cards are played . . . . The other gives the answer 5.

(4) After the first round, repeat the process, but this time each of you plays two cards.

Note to Teacher: Use two decks of playing cards with picture cards removed.

28. Learning Station 8: What Numbers Tell About You

Directions: Complete each of the following on the answer card
for this station

NUMBERS TELL ABOUT

1. Your height: _____ feet _____ inches _____
2. Your weight: _____ pounds
3. Your shoe size _____
4. Your hat size _____
5. Your vision _____
6. Your speed: number of seconds to run 25 feet _____
7. Your agility: number of seconds to deal 52 cards _____
8. Your jumping ability: number of feet you can jump _____

On the back of this card answer this question: Does this
information really tell anything about you?

29. Learning Station 9: What's Your Guess?

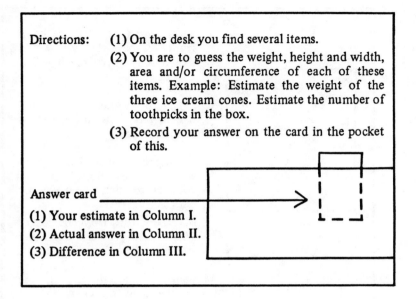

Directions: (1) On the desk you find several items.

(2) You are to guess the weight, height and width, area and/or circumference of each of these items. Example: Estimate the weight of the three ice cream cones. Estimate the number of toothpicks in the box.

(3) Record your answer on the card in the pocket of this.

Answer card

(1) Your estimate in Column I.

(2) Actual answer in Column II.

(3) Difference in Column III.

Note to the teacher: Plan to use several items for this station. For example, you could place some in several small ice-cream cartons so that you'll have items of different weight. Fasten lids securely with tape. Also, use a variety of objects such as golf balls, baseballs, soccer balls, wooden blocks, sticks or dowels, box of toothpicks, etc.

You will also have to provide students with the appropriate equipment to measure these items—scale, ruler, tape measure, etc.

30. Learning Station 10: Buy It

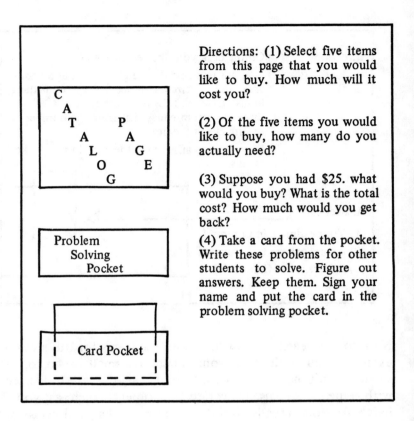

C
A
   T   P
      A   A
         L   G
            O   E
               G

Problem
   Solving
      Pocket

Card Pocket

Directions: (1) Select five items from this page that you would like to buy. How much will it cost you?

(2) Of the five items you would like to buy, how many do you actually need?

(3) Suppose you had $25. what would you buy? What is the total cost? How much would you get back?

(4) Take a card from the pocket. Write these problems for other students to solve. Figure out answers. Keep them. Sign your name and put the card in the problem solving pocket.

Note to the teacher: Tear a page from any order catalog and paste it on the learning station as shown. Have a student helper check the accuracy of the work of each student at this station (steps 1-3). Have students who complete other student problems (from problem solving pocket), find that student and compare answers. They should see you or your student helper if answers differ.

31. Learning Station 11: Math Practice

Directions: (1) Complete each of the following activities.

(2) Write your answers on the card provided. Be sure to put your name on the card.

(3) Take the card to the teacher or student helper for correction.

(4) Divide each number that is named in a given column by the number named at the top of that column.

5	6	4
45	48	28
30	30	4
15	54	36
10	6	8
40	18	16
35	24	24
5	12	32
20	36	12
25	42	20

(5)

$3 \times 2 = 6$	6 divided by 2 = 3
$3 \times 3 = 9$	9 " by 3 = 3
$3 \times 4 = 12$	12 " by 4 = 3
$3 \times 5 = 15$	15 " by 3 = 5
$3 \times 6 = 18$	18 " by 3 = 6

Select an equation and make up a word problem to illustrate it. Solve the problem. Ask one of your classmates to try it.

32. Learning Station 12: Station-Break Fractions

Directions: (1) Complete each of the following problems.
               (2) Put your answers on the card for this station.
               (3) Bring your completed card to the teacher or
                   student helper.

Use each of the fractions $\frac{0}{6}$ through $\frac{5}{6}$ in one and only one circle.

(a) Arrange the fractions so that the sum of the numbers named along each side of the triangle is 1.

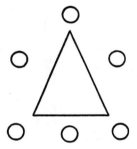

(b) Make rectangles like the one shown below. Color a fractional part of each shape.

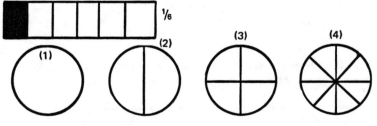

(c) Match the number over the circle with these fractional parts: one whole, thirds, halves, quarters. Now write these as fraction numbers.

(d) Using the circles in "C," what would one half of each be:
    (1)_____ (2)_____ (3)_____ (4)_____ (5)_____

33. Learning Station 13: Math Word-Detector

Directions: Take one sheet from the pocket.

(a) Find the listed words in the diagram. They are in all directions—forward, backward, up, down and diagonally.

Pocket
(8 x 10)

Note to the teacher: It is best to ditto the diagram and place enough copies in the pocket so that each student can select one and complete it.

Words in Puzzle

Fraction	Twenty
Polygon	Parallel
Multiply	Line
Square	Set
Segment	Parallelogram
Probability	Plane
	Zero

T	P	H	X	F	R	A	C	T	I	O	N	Y	T
T	Q	O	R	R	E	F	O	R	E	Z	T	W	E
E	N	A	L	P	Z	S	Q	U	A	I	A	S	L
K	M	U	J	Y	S	D	R	V	L	U	E	T	L
E	U	C	E	L	G	N	A	I	T	G	W	N	E
C	L	G	R	U	O	O	B	E	M	E	N	I	L
W	T	O	S	E	A	A	N	E	N	G	S	O	L
E	I	H	T	T	B	O	N	T	X	Q	L	N	A
L	P	X	D	O	C	T	Y	I	U	P	M	V	R
J	L	I	R	S	C	D	C	A	F	E	P	K	A
N	Y	P	B	L	I	K	R	Y	H	F	P	E	P
M	A	R	G	O	L	E	L	L	A	R	A	P	Z

34. Learning Station 14: Symbols and Signs

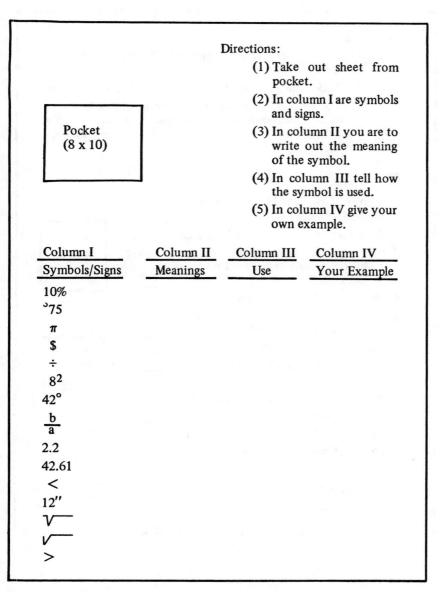

Directions:

(1) Take out sheet from pocket.

(2) In column I are symbols and signs.

(3) In column II you are to write out the meaning of the symbol.

(4) In column III tell how the symbol is used.

(5) In column IV give your own example.

Pocket (8 x 10)

Column I Symbols/Signs	Column II Meanings	Column III Use	Column IV Your Example
10%			
$^{\circ}75$			
π			
$			
$\div$			
8^2			
$42°$			
$\frac{b}{a}$			
2.2			
42.61			
$<$			
$12''$			
$\sqrt{\quad}$			
$\sqrt{\quad}$			
$>$			

Note to the teacher: Same as # 33.

35. Learning Station 15: Numbers in Sports: A Quiz

Directions:

    (1) Answer the following questions by numbering your station card from one to eight.

    (2) Check your answer with the teacher or a student helper.

    (3) Take another card and write three questions for other students to answer; sign it and place in problem-solving pocket. Be ready to give the correct answers to your questions.

<u>SPORTS QUIZ</u>

1. What number would you use for a double? ____

2. What number is awarded a field goal? ____

                                                     Card Pocket

3. How many points will you have if you made ten baskets and three foul shots in basketball? ____

4. What is a full count in baseball? ____

5. You have 15, I have "love." What number represents "love"? ____

6. Every time a football team makes a first down, it has gained at least ____ yards.

                                                     Problem Solving Pocket

7. How many wrestlers are usually in a tag team match? ____

8. How many men can be on the field for

    a baseball game ____

    a football game ____

    a soccer game ____

    a lacrosse game ____

36. Learning Station 16: Geometry—Shapes

Directions:

    (1) Take two or three pieces of poster paper. Use one for your base and the other for outlining.

    (2) Cut out the following and put on the poster paper. Label (identify) and cut out. Show your poster to the teacher or student helper to be sure all your cutouts are correct.

Cut out a: triangle
           closed curve
           pentagon
           octagon
           irregular hexagon
           square
           parallelogram

    (3) If you have room on your poster, try to find each of these in newspapers or magazine ads and/or pictures. Cut out and glue onto your poster.

37. Learning Station 17: Math Poetry

Directions:

(1) Try your skills at writing poetry about math concepts, principles and processes that we have been studying.

(2) First write out one or two poems on a sheet of paper; then, when you have them the way you want them, rewrite them on a piece of poster paper and tack up on the poetry board.

Here are two examples:

a) The commutative property of addition is part of this illustration.

That four plus two equals two plus four.

THAT'S IT FOLKS—THERE AIN'T NO MORE!!!

b) Another word for a couple might be duet.

But don't confuse a quart with a quarter.

38. Learning Station 18: Discovering Discounts

Directions: Many stores sell items at discount prices. Comparative shopping (looking for the best deal) can be of value to you provided the item you buy is a quality item.

Some people say you get what you pay for. What does this mean to you? Think about this when you do comparative shopping.

You should also learn to find the amount of discount and sales price. Learn to estimate. Here are some problems to help you.

| SALE |
| STEREO $115 |
| 20% OFF |
| TODAY ONLY |

To find the cost of this stereo, you would multiply the original price ($115) by the amount of the discount (20% = .20) and subtract the result from the original price

Fill in this flow chart to show how one finds the actual sales price on a discount item.

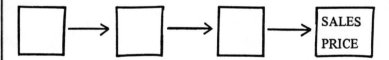

Complete these problems: Estimate first, then compute.

	SHOES	SKATES	JACKET	BICYCLE
Original Price	$14.95	$22.50	$29.99	$92.75
Discount Rate	10%	15%	12%	20%
Amount of Discount: Estimate				
Amount of Discount: Actual				
Sales Price: Estimate				
Sales Price: Actual				

39. Learning Station 19: Fractions

Directions: On your learning station cards, put your answers to the following problems. Use one card for each.

(a) For each of the following define the term and give an example. Use your textbook to help you.

(1) Numerator   (2) Denominator

(3) Fractional Number   (4) Equivalent fraction

(5) Mixed numeral   (6) Improper fraction

(7) Proper fractions   (8) Fractions in simplest form

(b) Make a number line for the following fractions:

1/2   1/4   1/3   5/6   1/7   3/4   2/7   5/9

40. Learning Station 20: Decimal Decision

Directions: 1. Solve the following decimal problems. Put your answer on your learning station card.

2. When you have completed this station, take your card to the teacher or student helper for correction.

(a) Write the correct number on your answer card:

(1) .66 _____ tenths _____ hundredths

(2) .076 _____ '' _____ '' _____ thousandths

(3) .432 _____ '' _____ '' _____ ''

(b) Complete the sequence:

(1)   .90   .60   .30   _____ _____ _____

(2)   1.2   1.4   2.2   2.4   _____ _____

(3)   1/4   .25   1/2   .50   _____ _____

(¢) Write in the correct symbol (<, > , =)

(1)   .12   2.1

(2)   .02   .20

(3)   .926   .732

(d) What's his average?

(1)   12 hits for 38 times at bat_____.

(2)   98 hits for 210 times at bat_____.

(3)   126 hits for 410 times at bat._____.

(e) Change each to a decimal number:

(1) $\dfrac{24}{100}$ (2) 9-2/5   (3) $\dfrac{26}{50}$

8   40 Group Games

When the One Great Scorer comes
    to write against your name—
He marks—not that you won or lost—
    but how you played the game.

Grantland Rice

In the classroom, the "how" of playing the game is more important than the game itself. The forty group games described in this chapter have been designed with certain objectives in mind.

First, the use of games to teach mathematics or any other subject provides opportunity for students to learn about themselves. They can sense in a game what is easy and what is difficult. They can experience possible consequences of trial and error.

Secondly, games provide an excellent opportunity to learn the value of rules and regulations that are so much a part of real life.

Third, games provide students with numerous opportunities for decision-making and problem-solving. Through games, students can learn the processes involved in solving a problem. The transfer to real life situations is obvious.

Fourth, we have found that the use of games illustrates our belief that learning can be enjoyable and that thinking is an exciting process.

Fifth, games promote the three "C's" that we have talked

about in the introduction to this book; namely, competition, communication and cooperation. Any teacher, using games will testify to the fact that students, in the competitiveness required by the game, will be demonstrating skills or cooperation and communication while they are trying to win the game. We think there is a very important point to be made here. We would only hope students are able to transfer it to the other games people play.

Finally, almost all mathematical concepts can be demonstrated or illustrated by games. In fact, one of the better ways to ensure retention is through games. For example, one objective of math instruction, at any level, is to help the learner develop a high level of efficiency in basic computation skills. Drill, or practice as it is now called, has been the way this has been accomplished in the past. However, research shows that drill or practice must be preceded by instruction that builds meaning and understanding.

The forty games that follow have been designed to meet the six objectives just described.

1. Postman (Entire class)

Arrange 30 chairs in 6 rows of 5 chairs each. These are to represent houses. Have a supply of blank envelopes available. Divide the class into two teams and have the children on Team A give directions for the children on Team B to execute. For example, the first child on Team A might say to the first child on Team B, "Take this letter to the third house on the second street." If the letter is delivered to the proper house, Team B receives one point. Next, the second child on Team A gives a direction to the second child on Team B, and so on, until all children have participated. Then the play is reversed, beginning with the first child on Team B giving a direction to the first child on Team A. At the end of the game, the team with the higher score is the winner.

2. It!!! (Entire class or small groups)

All players sit in a circle. The one who is "It" stands in the center of the circle and gives an addition combination (e.g., 5 + 2). The players are assigned numerals in such a way that each numeral occurs twice. Thus, if "It" calls "5 and 2," the two children assigned "7" try to change places before "It" can occupy one of their places.

3. Moving Man (Entire class)

Have several pupils line up across the front of the room, making sure each one knows his ordinal position in the line. Then choose a pupil, the "Moving Man," to stand at the back of the room facing away from the line. The "Moving Man" uses ordinals in giving directions to pupils to change places; for example, he might say, "The eighth pupil changes places with the tenth." The "Moving Man" must try to keep from moving a child more than once as long as possible. Whenever he does move a child more than once, he takes that pupil's place and the latter becomes the "Moving Man."

4. Moving On (Entire class)

The children are seated in a row of seats facing the teacher. When the teacher says, "Count off by eights," the first child says, "eight;" the second child says, "sixteen;" the third says, "twenty-four," etc., until some child makes a mistake. When this happens the one who misses must move to the front of the row and those who were formerly in front of him must shift back one seat. The teacher then asks for a new count off using a different number. When the game is ended the winner is the pupil who is sitting in the last seat at that time. The object is to keep moving back. One can progressively increase the difficulty of the numbers used.

5. Connections (Entire class)

Each of four to six players writes the numerals 1 through 10 on a sheet of paper, spreading the ten numerals all over the sheet in a random order and then drawing a ring around each of the numerals. Children then exchange papers according to a pre-arranged plan and on signal, begin connecting the ringed numerals in proper serial order. The first child finished calls "Connection," and is the winner if he has made no mistake.

6. Who Am I? (Entire class in teams)

One of 6 to 10 children is "It" and stands in the center of the group. He thinks of a number (e.g. 8) and then gives a "clue" to the other children in the group to see if they can determine the number selected. The child who is "It" might give one of the following clues: "I am the number that comes after 7. Who am I?" "I am the number that comes before 10 when counting by two. Who am I?" After the child who is "It" has given his clue, he calls on one of the children in the group to answer the question, "Who am I?" If the child called upon answers the question correctly, he becomes "It." If he answers incorrectly, another child is asked the question. Other clues can be given.

7. "Jumping" Math (Entire class)

Use when children are restless. Give a problem, e.g. 3 + 4. Have children "jump" out the answer. Subtraction, multiplication or division may also be used.

8. Good Shepherd (Small groups)

Have two piles of flash cards on which proper fractions of all sizes and often-used denominators have been written. The "good shepherd" tries to pick the fattest or largest sheep in the group. The players draw cards from the two piles and show the shepherd. He must decide which player holds the largest fraction. For each correct answer, the shepherd scores one point. When he misses, another shepherd takes his place, and the cards are then reshuffled.

9. Traveling (Teams or entire class)

Each "passenger" is assigned a number from 0 to 18. The "bus driver" calls out a basic combination, such as Street "7 plus 5." The child who has been assigned the number 12 must pay his fare by saying "12 Street." If he fails to respond immediately, the bus driver puts him off the bus. This game can be used for addition, subtraction, multiplication or division. Depending upon the knowledge of number facts of the group, players can be given more than one assigned number.

10. Number Facts (Teams, small groups or entire class)

"I am thinking of a number." One pupil thinks of a statement such as—"I am thinking of a number. If I add 3 to it, I will have 12. What is the number?" All may answer on paper, or one may answer orally. Team scores may also be kept. Use this activity for addition, subtraction, multiplication and division.

11. Time Around the World (Teams)

Arrange the players into rows. One row could represent Tokyo; a second row, San Francisco; a third, Denver; a fourth, New York; a fifth, London. On the blackboard write a specific time of day for their own city.

10 A.M.
4 P.M.
1 P.M.
    etc.

The players in each row would have to quickly calculate what the time is in the city they represent at each of the hours given. The pupils stand up as they finish. Check the order in which each row completes the problems. The winning row is the one which finishes most quickly and with the highest number of correct answers. On succeeding rounds, the rows change names.

12. Equilateral Triangles (Entire class)

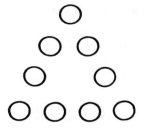

Use once only the numerals from 1 to 9 to make all sides have equal sums.

Here are three possible solutions:

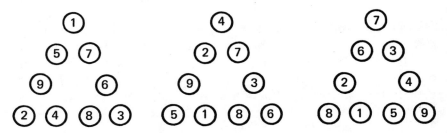

13. Parking Lot (Individuals or small groups)

This game is designed to put interest into the practice and mastery of 100 multiplication combinations. It consists of five "parking lots," graded in difficulty, and 100 cards, each of which contains a picture of a car on which is printed a multiplication product. Each "parking lot" provides spaces for twenty cars. Each space contains a multiplication combination, the answer to which appears on the printed card. The player places the cars in their correct parking places.

14. Number Detective (Entire class)

Have the class attempt to "decode" this message:

23-8-1-20	9-19	25-15-21-18	14-1-13-5?
(What	is	your	name?)

Code A = 1, B = 2, C = 3 . . . Z = 26

Other activities based on this idea are:

1. If A = 2 and B = 4, what number would you assign to C, D, E, etc.?
2. Write your school's name in number code.
3. Have each class member make up a code of his own and ask others to decode the message.

15. More Sleuthing (Entire class)

Have the class develop a number code of their own, using different number systems of the past and the present.

16. Baseball (Five teams of five or six students)

Divide the class into five teams. Have the teams give themselves a name. These five teams are the league. In this league, there will be a 25-game schedule. Each game will last seven innings. The team that wins the most games is the league champion. However, in order to win the Math World Series, the first and second place teams meet in a five game series.

Here is how the game is played. (Teachers may vary these procedures to fit their own needs and talents of students in their classes).

A. Prepare a stack of cards as follows:

> 15 cards with singles marked on them;
> 8 cards with doubles marked on them;
> 5 cards with triples marked on them;
> 4 cards with home runs marked on them.

B. Decide what team is the home team (coin flip is adequate).

C. Give the students on the home team copies of math books from the grade below them (this must be used in first three innings): their own grade level (to be used in innings 4 and 5); and one grade above level (to be used in innings 6 and 7).

D. Each student on the home team "pitches" a math question to a student on the team at bat.

E. The student at bat first draws a card from the "batter's box." Example: double.

F. The student on the home team (team that bats last) "pitches" a math question taken from the book. The batter can answer the question orally or complete it on the board. If he/she gets it right, it's a hit—a double. Wrong answers are out.

G. The game is played just like baseball for seven innings.

NOTE: a couple of teachers suggested that each team prepare a series of questions (about 50) before each game so that they don't have to be prepared during the game.

17. Golf Game (Entire class)

While pupils lay heads on desks with eyes closed, the teacher or leader writes a "story" problem on the board. At a signal "Go," all boys and girls look up, read the problem and begin work. As each pupil finishes, he raises his hand. The leader gives the first person who completes one point, the second two points, and so on. These represent the "strokes" taken to make the first "hole." Each pupil records his score at the left side of his paper. Those who cannot finish the problem in a reasonable time are given an arbitrary number of "strokes" larger than those of other members of the group. The problem is then worked at the board by a pupil. Those who had incorrect answers must add as many "strokes" to their scores as was given to those who did not finish. Nine "holes" constitute a "round." The lowest score wins.

18. Magic Squares (Entire class)

Study this square. Find the sum for each row, for each column, and for each diagonal.

8	1	6
3	5	7
4	9	2

Fill in the following squares to make them "magic" like the previous one.

8		4	(3)
1	5	9	
6	7		(2)

	1		7	(14, 12)
4	15	6	9	
5		3	16	(10)
11	8	13		(2)

19. Double Cross (Entire class)

Using this shape, and the numerals 1 through 12, many patterns of the double cross are possible for the sums of 26 in both rows and columns.

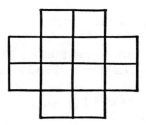

```
        12  11
    7   1   4   10
    8   3   2   9
        6   5
```

```
        6   7
    2   11  4   9
    3   1   10  12
        8   5
```

```
        5   7
    12  11  1   2
    3   4   10  9
        6   8
```

20. Magic Double Crosses (Entire class)

This activity can be used to stimulate interest or to work with specific abilities regarding numerals. Ask the student to make as many patterns of the sample double cross given him as possible. Use sums such as 22, 26, 31, etc., both in rows and in columns.

	12	11	
7	1	4	10
8	3	2	9
	6	5	

	5	7	
12	11	1	2
3	4	10	9
	6	8	

21. Modular Clocks (Entire class)

Use these puzzles to increase knowledge and skill in handling modular numbers and to demonstrate uses for modular numbers in daily life.

Mod 12 is familiar as our twelve-hour clock, so review with it first. Let pupils find the basic facts for various operations, beginning from any numeral on the clock. For example, using 12 as the starting or zero point, 6 plus 7 equals 1, 9 plus 6 equals 3, 7 less 4 equals 3, etc. Then use other numbers as a starting point.

Sample Puzzle items:

Starting on 1, on which clock does $2 + 4 = 0$? (Mod 7)
Starting on 4, on which clock does $9 - 2 = 5$? (Mod 6)
Starting on 5, on which clock does $3 - 1 = 0$? (Mod 7)
Starting on 0, on which clock does $-2 + 17 = 0$? (Mod 4, 5, 3)

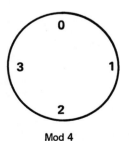

Mod 4

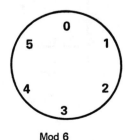

Mod 6

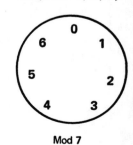

Mod 7

22. Number Bee (Entire class)

Divide the children into two teams. The teacher shows the first pupil on Team One the addition combination selected from a pack of addition-combination fact cards. If the right answer is given, the child gets the card. If the wrong answer is given, the first pupil on the other team is given a chance to respond correctly and may keep the card if his answer is correct. Continue in this way, alternating from one team to the other as combinations are selected and given. The team with the most cards in its possession at the end of the game is declared the winner. This game can also be used for subtraction, multiplication, division, fractions, etc.

23. The Coin Game (Teams)

Divide class into two teams. Have the first student on Team One give a list of names of coins, and have a member of the other team give the value in cents. For example, the first student might say, "One dime, one nickel, two pennies." He would then call on someone on Team Two to give the value in cents: 17 cents.

24. Spin-A-Sentence (Entire class or small groups)

This learning game is fun for pupils and offers practice and review in sentence formation. It may also be used as an aid in understanding word problems.

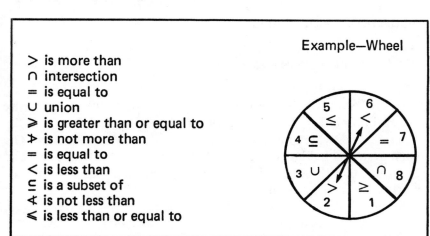

> is more than
∩ intersection
= is equal to
∪ union
≥ is greater than or equal to
≯ is not more than
= is equal to
< is less than
⊆ is a subset of
≮ is not less than
≤ is less than or equal to

Have the students play this game in groups of two or three. One student from a team spins the wheel. The other team must make up two problems using (first) the symbols on the wheel and (second) the numbers on the wheel or multiples of those numbers.

The team must answer or solve the problems created by the other team. Each team gets its points when both problems are answered correctly: three points when one problem is answered correctly; no points for incorrect answers. The team to earn fifty points first wins the game.

25. Bouncing Ball (Teams)

Select teams, the number on each team depending upon the maximum size of the sum to be encountered with the addition facts given. For example, if sums do not exceed seven, then have teams of seven. Assign a numeral from 1 to 7 to each child on each team. Have the children arrange themselves in random order in a circle, with the teacher or one of the children in the center. The person in the center calls out an addition combination, such as "4 and 2," and at the same time bounces a rubber ball in the center of the circle. The opposing team members who have been assigned the number 6 (the sum 4 and 2) try to run out and catch the ball before it bounces a second time. The one who succeeds scores a point for his or her team. Play continues in this way for a specific length of time or number of turns. The team with the higher number of points is the winner. This game can also be used with subtraction, mixed addition, etc.

26. "It" Game (Entire class)

"It" stands behind the chair of one of the children who are seated in a circle. The teacher shows a question card. "It" and the child behind whom he stands compete to answer correctly. The winner stands behind the chair of the next child in the circle and the game continues. This activity can be used for any mathematical facts currently under study.

27. Highest Bidder (Entire class)

The teacher may start by saying, "Going, going for 3 factorial." The pupil says, "Gone for 6." The teacher then continues by saying, "And going, going for 4 factorial." Another pupil says, "Gone for 24." The teacher continues by saying, "Going for 5 factorial." The teacher may begin another exercise by saying, "Going for 5^0." The pupil answers, "Gone for 1." Teacher then continues, "Going for 5^2." This activity keeps the class alert to think in higher terms each time around.

28. Train Conductor (Entire class)

Play the game of "Train" with cards bearing such equations as $7 + 8 = 15$, $12 - 6 = 6$, and $8 + 9 = 17$. One child who is the conductor stands next to the desk of another child. The teacher holds up a card; both children try to give the answer to the equation. If the conductor gives the correct answer first, he moves on to the next child. He continues to be conductor as long as he gives the answer first. When another child responds with the correct answer first, he is the new conductor. The winner continues around the room until he misses. Children who give an incorrect answer may be "switched" to a side track to study the missed combination. They can rejoin the "train" by giving the correct answer to a card missed by another student.

29. "Countingman" (Entire class)

Help each child make a pair of Countingman cards. Duplicate the picture of the Countingman on 8″ x 11″ pieces of paper. Have the children color and paste them on heavy cardboard, or you may prefer to provide stencils of the Countingman so the children can draw directly on cardboard or tagboard. Have them label one card the Tens-man and the other card the Ones-man. Then help the children cut out brightly colored paper, or provide small flat sticks to be used as fingers. Give each child an envelope in which to store the fingers. Place a number of objects on the flannel board, and have the children record the count on their Countingman cards. Hold up a numeral and have the children show the number it represents by placing fingers on the Countingmen.

TENS

ONES

30. "I Went to the Store" (Teams)

The first player says, "I went to the store and bought a marble for 3 cents." The second child says, "I went to the store and bought a marble for 3 cents and a top for 5 cents. I spent 8 cents." Each player in turn must add one item and give the total amount spent. Begin again each time a player fails to give the right answer.

31. Quick Operations (Teams)

Write a column of numbers on the board and ask the pupils to write the same value in four different forms, using a different operation in each. For example,

$72 = 8 \ \times \ 9; 36 + 36; 144 - 72; 216 \div 3$

$25 = 5^2; 35 - 10; 100 \div 4; 18 + 7$

Have teams operate this game as a relay race.

32. High Finance (Small groups)

Use the old standby game of Monopoly to explain interest rates, buying and selling, renting, etc. Don't overlook other games being sold commercially that use mathematics.

33. Old Maid (Small groups)

Use paired number facts, equations, fractions, etc.—one on each card. Provide one card with no match. The player left with the no-match card loses the game.

34. Ninety-Nine (Large groups)

This card game is played with standard decks of cards. It can be played with any number of participants, but is best when held to no more than a dozen players. Each player is dealt three cards; the rest of the cards compose the draw pile. The first player lays down a card face up and declares its value.

$3 = 99$

$4 = $ Reverse

$9 = $ Hold

$10 = -10$

Ace $= 1$

Jack $= 10$

Queen $= 10$

King $= 10$

All other cards are face value

The object of the game is *not to exceed* 99. If a player cannot lay down a card which is less than 99, the player is eliminated. This game can be continued until only one pupil is left in the game. This player is declared the winner.

35. Wheel of Fortune (Entire class, small groups, teams)

Pupils should construct a wheel for reviewing multiplication facts:

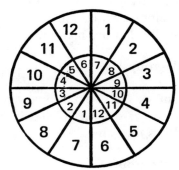

The outer wheel is stationary, the inner one is movable, allowing for all combinations. This same principle can be used for other mathematical functions. Team games can be devised using this tool.

36. Math Bingo (Entire class)

Develop "Bingo Cards" using number combinations appropriate to the content under study.

Example: Subtraction

Slips of paper, each marked for one of the whole numbers 0 through 9, are mixed and placed in a box. When, for example, the slip marked 4 is drawn, the squares marked 6-2, 8-4, and 9-5 on the card would be covered. Many different cards can be made and the game played in traditional bingo manner or played until someone covers all the squares. Allow pupils to copy the cards for playing the game at home if they choose.

37. Coordinate Geometry (Teams)

Let children play the game "Find the Treasure." Two

children from the challenging team should draw a picture of an island on a coordinate grid. They may "hide" a treasure on the "island." The treasure should be identified by three points which may be in a line (vertical, horizontal or diagonal) or be the corner points of a triangle.

Children then take turns calling out names for coordinate points (5, 2, etc.), and on another coordinate grid, mark an X at the point called. The object is to locate the treasure of the other team. When a called point falls on part of the island, the opponent must say, "You are on my island." When any portion of the treasure is "hit" by a called point, the game is over and another one is started.

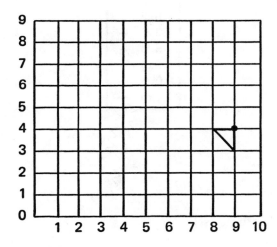

38. Dice Game (Teams)

Roll the dice (real or made up). Name at least two common multiples of the numbers. Establish a time limit for players. Award points for correct answers; the team with the most points wins the game. Dice can be used for addition, subtraction or multiplication, or a game can be devised using all of the above. Addition and subtraction equations can also be formed.

39. Test Your Strength (Teams)

On the chalkboard, draw a "strength-testing machine" such

as the one shown below. Attach a piece of red crepe paper at the bottom. Each pupil is to "test his strength." Each time he gives a correct answer he pulls the paper up one step. The object is to get the paper to the top by giving all the correct answers. Keep score. The team with the high score wins.

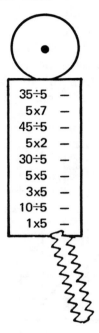

40. Puzzlers (Entire class)

Use each of the digits 1, 2, 3, 4, 5, and 6 in only one of the following circles so that the sum along each side of the triangle is ten. There are several correct solutions.

Problem   Possible solution

Use each of the digitis 1 through 9. Place the digit 5 in the center square. Place even numbered digits in the corners. Use the remaining digits in the squares that remain so that the sum of each row and each column is 15. There are several correct solutions.

Problem

even		even
	5	
even		even

Possible solution

2	9	4
7	5	3
6	1	8

Use each of the digits 1 through 9 in only one of the circles below so that the sums along each side of the triangle is 21. There are several correct solutions.

Problem

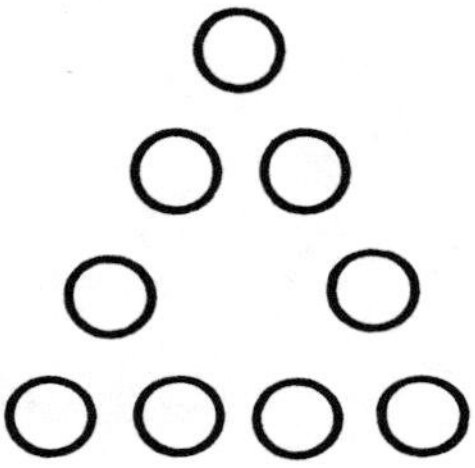

Possible Solution

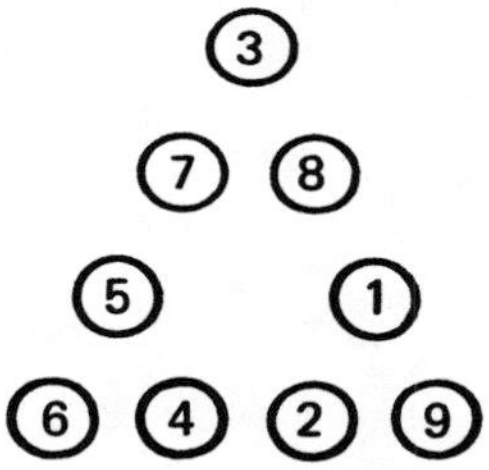

③
⑦ ⑧
⑤   ①
⑥ ④ ② ⑨

Have youngsters develop "puzzlers" of their own to exchange with other students.

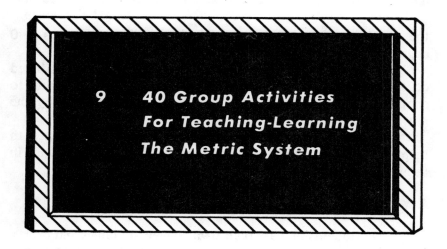

9   40 Group Activities
For Teaching-Learning
The Metric System

America is going metric and all of us, young and old, will have to learn to live in a metric world. It will probably be much easier for the younger learners than it will be for the older ones.

Some background information dealing with the metric system will be of value as teachers and learners begin to use this system.

During the eighteenth century, the metric system was developed by the French. It was a decimal system based upon the meter. It began to replace the common English units—feet, yards and pounds—particularly among scientists and technicians. Eventually, the metric system was adopted for common use in most countries. In the United States, the metric system is used by scientists, but not as yet by the populace. However, as everyone now knows, it is only a matter of time before it will prevail. Most textbooks now provide content about the metric system.

In summary, the *meter* is the basic metric unit. When the meter is divided into ten equal parts, each part is called a *decimeter*. Divide the decimeter into ten equal parts and you have *centimeters*. Do the same to centimeters and each unit is called a *millimeter*.

The centimeter is the basic unit of length; the gram is the basic unit of weight; the cubic centimeter is the basic unit of volume. A kilometer is 1000 meters. To measure temperature in the metric system the Celsius scale is used: water freezes at 0 degrees and boils at 100 degrees.

The major advantage of the metric system is that it is based on the ten numeration system. Thus changing from one unit to another is easy because one either multiplies or divides by the power of ten.

The teaching-learning activities that follow are designed to help students learn the metric system and develop confidence in using the system.

1. Metric Table

Have students prepare their own conversion tables and charts. When these are available to each student, have them work on one unit per week so that they begin to "think metric." For example, the first week can focus on temperature (Celsius); second week distance (kilometers), etc. This can be repeated every five or six weeks.

2. Providing a Rationale

A group of students can look up and report to the entire class the arguments set forth by some groups in the United States for the adoption of the metric system for all measurements. They can also arrange a bulletin board exhibit of articles in newspapers and magazines which make reference to the metric system.

3. Going to the Source

Have a class representative write to the National Bureau of Standards, Washington, D.C. for information about their work, function, etc. Have them inquire about Public Law 90-472 dealing with the Metric System.

4. Units of Distance

A meter is the basic unit of distance in the metric system. There are 100 centimeters (centi—100) in a meter. There are 10 millimeters in a centimeter. In the metric systems, units are changed by multiplying or dividing by 10, 100 or 1000. Obtain a meter stick from the high school science teacher and let the class examine it. Have students discuss the advantages of using multiples of 10 as compared to the English system. Each student should make a chart comparing the English system's and the metric system's units of distance. Youngsters can make a cardboard ruler using the centimer and the millimeter.

5. Getting Answers

Have students write to other students in foreign countries for an explanation of the metric system.

6. Why?

Have a student find out from a scientist why all scientists use the metric system.

7. Measuring Things

Help the children make a giant measuring tape by using adding machine paper. The yards can be marked in blue, the feet in red, and the inches in black. On the same paper, use the metric conversions along the English measures. Have children use this tape to measure such things as the playground, hall, or classroom. Display the tape on the wall of the classroom for future reference. Whenever the children read of a giant whose feet are ten feet long or a rabbit that can jump seven feet into the air, refer them to the measuring tape and have them give the distance in metric terms.

8. How Big?

Using the meter as the unit of distance, prepare a chart asking students to find the length of the following:

	English	Metric
Football field	_____	_____
One-mile racetrack	_____	_____

	English	Metric
Baseball diamond	_____	_____
Etc.	_____	_____

9. How Close?

Have pupils use a meter stick to measure the lengths of various objects to the nearest millimeter, to the nearest centimeter, to the nearest decimeter, and to the nearest meter.

10. More Measurement

Have pupils measure the lengths of several objects by using the inch as the unit of measure. For each measurement have pupils obtain an equivalent measurement in which the unit of measure is the foot. Repeat the activity by having pupils use the yard as the unit of measure. Have pupils repeat this activity substituting the meter, decimeter and centimeter. Compare the results.

11. Abbreviations—Symbols—Prefixes

Have students make a list of the abbreviations and symbols used in the metric system such as; cm., m., mm., dm., 1., g. What do they mean? Students should become aware of the difference between abbreviations and symbols. Have them study the prefixes used in metric measure and make a list:

tera-

giga-

mega-

kilo-

hecto-

deka-

deci-

centi-milli-

micro-

nano-

pico-

femto-

atto-

Ask: Which ones are commonly used? Which ones are used more infrequently for specific measurements?

12. Using a Ruler

Have students use a plastic centimeter ruler or one that they have made to measure various objects in the classroom. Use desk tops, pencils, books, etc. for this assignment.

13. What's Best?

Have pupils measure some simple closed figures in the classroom. Then have them decide if a square inch, a square foot, or a square yard would be the best to determine the area of each of these figures. Have them repeat this procedure using metric measures. This will present an interesting problem in as much as centimeters, decimeters and meters will have to be squared!

14. Squares!

To help pupils visualize the relationships between the number of square inches in a square foot, the number of square feet in a square yard, and the number of square inches in a square yard, have pupils use nine pieces of cardboard (each one square foot) to build a square yard as shown below.

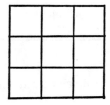

Have pupils tell the number of square inches in a square foot (144), the number of square feet in a square yard (9), and the number of square inches in a square yard (1296). Have students repeat as above using centimeters, decimeters, and meters. Compare results.

15. Metric Distance

Have pupils bring in road maps of their state. After choosing a route between two cities, have the pupils determine the distance using kilometers. Does it take you longer to get there? Write open sentences that can be solved to determine the distance between those two cities over the route chosen. Solve the open sentences to determine the distance.

Another related activity could be determining the amount of gasoline used in making a given trip. If, for example, you use 16 gallons of gasoline, you will have used 60 liters.

16. How Far and How Fast?

Have youngsters make road signs indicating the distance to another town. Have them make road signs indicating the "metric" distance. Example:

English

```
Middletown
25
Miles
```

Metric

```
Middletown
40
Kilometers
```

Have youngsters make replicas of automobile speedometers. Have them represent the same speeds in both English and metric measures. Example:

English

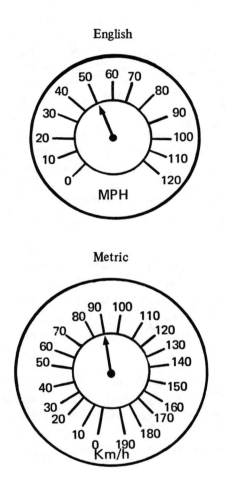

Metric

17. Sports and Games

Have students investigate and record all the events in the Olympic Games and the measure used in these events.

In addition, have the students illustrate what will happen when some of our games, such as football, are changed to the metric system. For example, how will the sports announcer say, "He's tackled on the forty yard line?"

18. Conversion Made Simple

Some companies are now producing steel rulers which provide both English and metric measures. They are the pull-out type which are handy, especially when used in construction activities. Have youngsters build a birdhouse, bird feeder, diorama, etc., and describe their use of this device in both English and metric terms.

19. Krypton 86

Investigate the meaning of "Krypton 86." Students should discover that this is an inert, colorless gaseous element which produces wavelengths that are the basis for defining the meter in the metric system. Its preciseness makes it an excellent way to define an international unit of measurement.

20. How Big Am I?

Using a tape measure which employs the metric system (centimeters), have students record their height, waist measurements, hat size, etc. How do these differ from the English system? Is there really a difference in size?

21. Sizes!

Obtain a French or German merchandise catalog and have students use the metric system to decide what sizes they wear in the various types of merchandise. Use a standard American tape measure and convert, and then use a centimeter tape measure. Compare findings with the system we now use.

22. Other Ways To Measure

Borrow a gram scale from a high school to show units of weight in the metric system. Have youngsters make their own balance scales.

23. Check Your Medicine Cabinet!

Have students bring in various vitamin bottles with the labels on them. Ask the students to note the units of weight. Example: 2 mg., 1 g., 20 mg. Why is the metric system used in describing what each tablet supplies?

24. How Heavy?

Have each pupil weigh himself on a scale and record the measurement in pounds. Then have each pupil figure out how much he weighs in ounces and record the measurement in ounces. Have everyone weighed convert their weight into kilograms (0.45 kilograms to a pound), then into grams (28.35 grams to an ounce).

25. Weighing Things

Have all pupils make lists of things that are usually bought by the ounce, pound and ton. Name these things in lists on the board. Using metric conversions, what would these things weigh?

26. Tons

Have students find the weight in pounds of different makes of cars. Have the weight of each make expressed in tons and pounds, and list them on a bulletin board. Use this activity to develop the meaning of the "metric ton," which is the measure of weight equal to 1,000 kilograms, or roughly the equivalent to 2,200 pounds.

27. Inquiry

Have a group of students investigate the "Treaty of the Meter" or the "Convention du Metre." This is a treaty signed by 18 nations in 1975 dealing with metric measures. One of the participants is the United States.

28. A Challenge!

Give students mathematical problems using the metric system. For example, have them find the circumference of a circle or the area of a rectangle.

29. Liters and Grams

Obtain European cookbooks. Recipes call for ingredients measured by using the standards of *liters* and *grams*. Specialty shops in many cities carry measuring cups, etc., using this standard. If someone can be recruited to translate the directions, preparing a simple dish from the cookbook would be a fine way to put this into practice.

30. Calibrating!

If a metric measuring cup can be obtained, have youngsters calibrate other containers. This will provide the classroom with an unlimited supply of metric measuring devices in a vast variety of sizes and shapes, as well as providing the youngsters with a valueable learning experience.

31. Party Time

Have a party. Using different juices and colored drinks, help students decide on the number of drinks they want to serve. Have them determine how many milliliters, liters, etc., they will have to provide.

32. Compare "Cups"

Using a *liter and/or gram* measuring cup, test the results against a standard American measuring cup. What is the difference?

33. Fun With Recipes

Take a simple recipe from an American cookbook and rewrite it, using metric measures.

34. How Hot Is It?

Have the students read the temperature of the classroom from a Fahrenheit thermometer. Now have them read the temperature from a Celsius (formerly known as a centigrade) thermometer. Is there a difference? Why? Have students investigate the differences between a Fahrenheit and Celsius thermometer. What is the freezing point of water of each? (F: $32°$, C: $0°$) What is the boiling point of water of each? (F: $212°$, C: $100°$) Ask them to find out why scientists use Celsius thermometers. Do students have ideas concerning the advantages of using a Celsius thermometer?

35. Make Your Own!

Have a group of students make Fahrenheit and Celsius thermometers to be used for a class demonstration. Make color scales as well as numerical scales.

36. Collect Labels

Have youngsters check their own kitchen cupboards for labels, boxtops, etc., that indicate weight by grams. It is surprising how many companies indicate both English and metric weights to inform the public of the amount in the container they are buying. Have them bring in labels, etc., and have them prepare a bulletin board or display using these presentations.

37. How Much?

Have students determine the price per gram of different foodstuffs using the labels collected in the previous activity. Is the price the same when using the English system? Repeat the activity using the English system.

38. Community Resources

Have someone (perhaps a parent), come into the classroom to explain how some professions—druggists, chemists, etc.—use metric measures in their work.

39. Estimating

Compile a list of commonly used items (as long or as short as appropriate), and have youngsters determine the proper unit of measurement to be used. Have them estimate the answers, then verify the answers by actually measuring the items.

Examples:

a. the capacity of a milk carton,
b. the diameter of a wastebasket,
c. the area of a desk top,
d. the amount of water the classroom could hold if it were turned into a swimming pool,
e. etc.

40. Plant a Metric Garden

With today's great interest in home gardening, most newspapers and home magazines carry articles to assist in planning such a project. These usually appear in late winter or early spring. Plan a real garden, a sand-table mini garden, or a "paper" garden. Use only metric measurement.

1. Determine the area of the land to be used.
   Example:

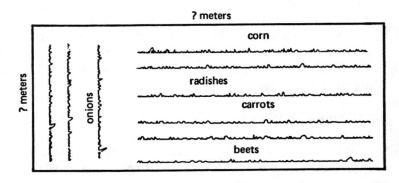

2. Decide what will be planted in the garden and how much of each thing will be planted.
3. Determine maximum height of the mature plants and arrange so that taller plants will not shade out smaller ones.

4. Figure out the distance required between rows; between plants.

5. Determine the amount (weight) of seeds that will be required.

6. Convert the recommended depth at which the seeds need to be planted.

7. Use degrees Celsius to decide when certain seeds should be put into the ground.

8. How much fertilizer will be needed?

9. How much water will be needed?

10. How much produce should this garden plot yield?

11. Have youngsters think up other ways to measure things related to their metric garden.

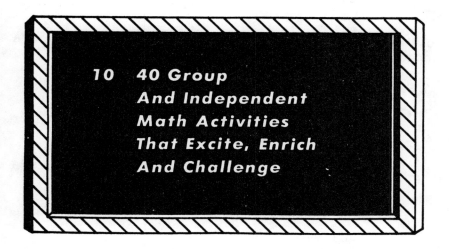

One of the major goals in education is self-direction in the learning process; or to put it another way, helping students to learn how to learn. It is obvious that this goal can only be attained when students are provided opportunities to practice this skill at school as well as at home.

How does the teacher put this goal into practice? The answer to this question is rather straightforward—the teacher creates learning activities that require a student or small group of students to solve personal, social and/or subject-matter problems with a minimum of assistance from the teacher. The teacher changes his/her role from that of a "transmitter" or "answer man" to that of a "learning manager.'"

Thus the emphasis in this chapter is on learning activities that require an individual or small group to learn math on their own. The purpose is to promote an independent study of certain mathematical concepts, principles and problems.

Teachers can use the forty activities in this chapter in a variety of ways—as enrichment for material in the text; as weekly assignments, one activity assigned per week for the entire year; as homework; as things to do when the students say there is nothing to do. Teachers should point out to students that these activities provide opportunities for self-direction and independent study.

Here, then, are the forty math activities that we hope help

you attain the objectives of this chapter; namely, to provide opportunities for students to learn some math on their own.

1. Sets and Subjects

Have individual students or small groups (three or four students) complete the following chart:

Sets—Subjects	Define	Example
Finite sets		
Infinite sets		
Empty sets		
Single element sets		
Equivalent sets		
Universal sets		
Subsets		
Equal sets		
Overlapping sets		
Disjoint sets		

2. Set Operations

To continue with the concept of sets and subsets, indicate to the students that there are three basic operations used to solve problems involving sets: union, intersection and complement.

Have students diagram examples of each operation. Also, have the students write the operation and the mathematical terms (e.g., A∪B = 1234). Finally, ask the students to find out why these diagrams are called *Venn diagrams*.

3. Math Mates

Together with other teachers, arrange a program whereby students in the upper grades can serve as teacher aides or math-mates. The emphasis in this kind of teaching program should not only be to provide remediation but also to have youngsters with obvious math ability in the upper grades work with lower grade children who seem to have potential math talent.

4. Double-Cross Puzzle

Provide students with one example of a "double-cross" and then have them make several of their own and exchange with one another.

You may ditto as many patterns as you wish and you may vary the numerals. Here is one example.

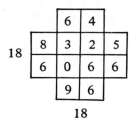

Using the numerals 0 through 9, how many patterns of "double-cross" are possible for the sums of 18 in both rows and columns?

5. Math Personality of the Month

Have a small group of students prepare a calendar that identifies the math men and women of the month.

The student should identify the person, his/her birth and death dates, contribution, etc.

For example:

Leonardo Fibonacci: Fibonacci series- 1,1,2,3,5,8,13,21, . . .

Problem: What is the pattern to the series? (each number in sequence is sum of previous two numbers). Students can also provide a brief biographical sketch of each person.

6. The Math Scientist

Mathematics is closely allied to the field of science. Scientists use math. To illustrate this point and to have students study the lives of scientists and inventors, ask a small group of youngsters to investigate this relationship between science and math.

Here is one example of how they might go about completing this task:

    (a) make a booklet or several booklets on this topic; give each booklet an appropriate title.

    (b) on each page of the booklet, identify the scientist and/or inventor and dates of birth and death; follow this with a short biographical sketch; then state the person's work and/or invention; conclude with the math implications or math use.

7. Math Riddles

Ask a small group of youngsters to help you gather a list of math riddles for the class. These can be placed on 3 x 5 cards and used whenever you or the class need to "fill in" some time or need a break. Here are two examples:

    (a) What has six feet and sings? (a trio)

    (b) How can you spell the opposite of difficult in two letters? (E-Z)

8. Math Formulas

There are math formulas for computing area, circumference, perimeter, volume and the like. Have a small group of students find math formulas and prepare a bulletin board for their class-mates that shows the formulas, what they mean and how they are used. In addition, have this group prepare problems, using each formula, for their classmates to solve.

9. What's the Angle?

There are several types of angles that can be introduced to students—right angles, obtuse angles, acute angles, etc.

Ask a small group of students to review the contents in

textbooks at their grade level, as well as grade levels above and below their grade level for a report on what is written about angles.

Ask the group to prepare a series of overhead transparencies that can be used for reporting their findings to the class. Have them include in the series of transparencies activities that their classmates can do as they proceed on their report on "what's the angle?"

10. Games

Have a small group of students arrange a display of commercial games that they have collected from their homes. Have the group summarize the math principles and computations that are part of the basic functions for playing the game.

11. Math Fair

Arrange a math fair for your class or school that is entirely student planned and operated. Have the students select a "math fair steering committee." Have this committee plan the fair by using a subcommittee pattern. Each subcommittee (three or four students) is designed according to certain tasks and functions it is to carry out. The chairman of each subcommittee reports to the "steering committee." For example, the steering committee might arrange the following subcommittees: a) physical facilities, b) program, c) special events, d) invitations, e) special needs, etc.

12. Math and Occupations

Have a small group of students study the occupations of mothers and fathers of students in your class or in the school. The purpose of this study should be to find out what resources parents may be able to provide and to determine how parents use math in their occupations.

Students should prepare a survey sheet and/or card that is designed so that the information they want is easily obtained. The results of these sheets can be used (a) as a resource for the teachers in the schools and (b) as part of a report on math made to students in the class.

13. Math Machines

Have a small group of students prepare a bulletin board display of machines that use numbers, compute, etc. Among the machines displayed should be computers, calculators, an abacus, clocks, watches, radio (dial), etc. The group should identify the pictures and provide a short description on why each is a "math machine."

14. Model Making

A small group of students should be asked to make models of pyramids, cones, cylinders, etc., that can be used when these items are to be studied. The students can also bring in examples of each of these, such as an ice-cream cone (cone), balloon (sphere), can (cylinder), cereal box (prism).

This group of students could also set up a table with numbered items such as a straw, baseball, globe, show box, funnel, etc., Each student is given a sheet appropriately numbered. They view the items on the table and mark on their sheet what kind of figure it is. Then they take their sheets to one of the group members to be corrected.

15. Math Glossary

Have a small group of students design a skills kit (use 5 x 8 cards) on math words used in their textbooks and other resources.

The kit should be arranged in alphabetical order or by sections (function section, angle section, etc.). Following the information cards (example: angle—two rays with the same endpoint) should be two or three activity cards.

16. Probability

There is a 60 percent chance of rain. This is a probability statement—a number telling how likely it is that a certain event will happen.

Ask a small group of students to guess the probability of the number of heads one will get when flipping a coin fifty times.

Have them try it and record the results as follows: fraction part 32 out of 50 = $\frac{32}{50}$; show a percentage = 64%.

Give the students several experiments to complete such as:

(a) Place 5 dimes and 3 nickels in a small box. Shake it.

(b) Draw one coin from the box. Tally it on chart below. Put it back in the box.

(c) Do this 50 times. Is your fraction for dimes close to 5/8—62 percent?

(d) Is your fraction for nickels close to 3/8—3 percent?

	TALLY	FRACTIONS	%
DIMES			
NICKELS			

Have the students design a number of experiments like this one (consult textbook also) for their classmates.

17. Holiday Math

Ask one or more small groups of students to help you design some interesting math activities—games that the class can do around special holidays such as Halloween, Thanksgiving, Christmas, Easter, Arbor Day, Mother's Day, Groundhog Day, Memorial Day, and the like.

Prepare a file for these activities and/or games and use when appropriate.

18. How Near? How Far?

Many students travel during the summer months. Have a small group of students survey the class and prepare a set of overhead transparencies that should show the results of their survey as follows: (1) places visited, (2) greatest distance from city, (3) average distance from city, (4) type of transportation, (5) length of visit, etc.

19. Bar Graphs

Ask a small group of students to check their math texts to find out how to design a bar graph. Then have this group investigate the cost of postal rates over the past twenty years and prepare a bar graph and explain it to the class.

Another small group might prepare a bar graph on the cost of bus transportation; another might do the same activity on the cost of gasoline.

20. Word Problems

Ask several small groups of students to help you design word problems for the class. Assign each small group one or two chapters from their textbook. For each chapter have the group design at least ten word problems based on the math concepts and principles appearing in that chapter. They should not use the word problems already in print.

21. Time Lines

Have three small groups of students make three time lines with wire across the classroom. One time line should be designated the social studies time line; another the science time line; the third the math time line. Each group is responsible for one of the time lines.

Punch holes in a group of 3 x 5 cards. Open up paper clips so that one end can be attached to the card and the other end placed on the wire. Have each group use streamers to mark the line wire as follows:

On each of the cards, each group is to mark significant social studies, science and math work. For example, math cards would include Euclid's Elements (300 B.C.)—with one side of the card being the title and a sketch. The back side of the card would describe the importance and meaning. Other math cards would include Oughtred, Descartes, Pythagoras, Pascal, Eratosthenes Newton, etc.

22. Sport Scores

Have a small group of students prepare a chart for the class that describes how numbers, numeration and computation are used in a variety of sports. The chart may be designed as follows:

GAME	SCORING	EXAMPLE	PT. SYSTEM	COMPUTATION
Football	Most points	21-14	Field goal—3 pts. Safety—2 pts. Touchdown—6 pts.	Addition
Golf	Least points	72	Least Number of shots per hole	Addition
Baseball				
Basketball				
Soccer				

23. Sport Term Quiz

Another interesting activity for a small group of students is an investigation into the terminology used in sports with math implications. There are a variety of ways that a small group of students could investigate this activity, but the one suggested here involves the small group and the class.

This group can collect a variety of sport terms and place them on cards. All of the cards are placed in a box. A student from the class selects a card and uses a blackboard to explain the term on the card. If the student does not answer correctly or leaves out information, one member of the small group then provides the answer or additions to the answer given.

Here are some examples of sport terms for one sport only—golf: eagle, par, birdie, bogey, double bogey.

24. Estimating

Have a small group of students cut out pictures from magazines and sales catalogs that include toys, appliances, sporting goods, clothes, cars, etc.

Have them paste each picture to a piece of cardboard. On the back of the card they should write the actual price of the item.

Each member of the group holds up a card and selects three students to estimate the cost of the item. The student coming closest to the actual cost of the item stays up and two other students are selected to estimate the cost of the item in next picture. After every member of the class has had a turn, the student who was "up" the longest wins. "Ties" should be played off by having students estimate the actual cost of the item in the picture, but this time including a 15 percent discount.

25. Order in the Court

Have a small group of students make transparencies for the overhead projector titled "Order in the Court." Each transparency should include a series of numbers in random order. Students in the class are to put the numbers in order and then explain the basis for their ordering.

Here are examples of two transparencies:

205 A.D.	600 B.C.
390 B.C.	400 A.D.
1225 B.C.	1440 B.C.
1836 B.C.	1776 B.C.

ignition, blastoff in minus 6 minutes blastoff minus 10 hours, blastoff minus 3 minutes, blastoff minus 10 seconds

26. State Math Trip

Have a small group collect state maps for each student in class. To help their classmates develop skills in finding the distance between geographical locations and in using scale mileage maps, have the group design a series of problems for the class.

For example, the group may select two places to visit in their state. One member of the group begins the experience as follows:

"We are leaving our school to go the _____ . How far is it from our school to this place?" (Students estimate mileage and record figures on their maps.) "Now let me tell you something about our first stop." (Student then explains why they stopped at the place, what they could do, see, enjoy. Historical information might also be provided.)

Another student in the small group takes the class to the second stop, asks the questions about mileage and provides the information about the place. This process continues until all ten places have been "visited." Students can compare total mileage and cost for gas if they went by car, school bus, etc.

27. Math Field Trips

You can design several math field trips for several of your small groups. One group can take a math field trip to their local newspaper, another to the airport, another to the bank, another to the weather station.

For example, a math field trip to the airport would require answering the following questions (all of which should be asked by students before their trip, whether real or imaginary):

1. What is the cost of a first-class ticket to major cities (to be identified)?
2. What is the cost to the same cities if one flies coach? What does one get for the difference in price?
3. How many runways does the airport have? How long are they?
4. How many flights come in each day? Fly out? Originate at the airport?
5. What kind of planes use the airport?
6. How many airlines use the airport?
7. How many people fly in or out in a week? month? year?
8. What is the cost of running the airport per month? year?
9. How many people are employed at the airport that do not work for the airlines?

10. What instruments are used at the airport to help with the flights? Who "mans" the instruments? What do the instruments do?

28. Math Tools

Have a small group of students design "mockups" and lessons for tools their classmates can use in mathematics. The mockups can be drawn on large pieces of construction paper, with lessons and actual tools beside the mockup for use by students. Lessons and designs should be made for such tools as protractor, compass, yardstick, meter stick, scale, thermometer, ruler, slide rule.

29. Lines and Symbols

Have a small group of students prepare a slide presentation (make their own slides) on the use of lines and symbols. For example, the presentation might begin with a slide on lines, and progress into symbols:

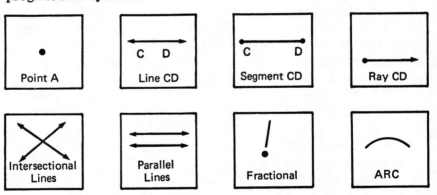

This group may also prepare a cassette tape explaining each frame so that their classmates can use the presentation independently.

30 Histograms

A histogram is a procedure for stressing the history and record of something in graph form. All students should be able to make and interpret histograms. To accomplish this objective students need to know about frequency and frequency tables for grouped and ungrouped data.

We have had excellent success by selecting a small group of students to investigate the use and construction of histograms. To do this, provide this group with several math textbooks that contain material about histograms. Ask the group to develop several lessons for their classmates on the purpose and use of histograms, with each lesson concluding with a review and some activity. You'll be surprised with the results. Also, have students explore articles describing the uses of histograms. We recommend Michael B. Leyden's article "Histograms and Raisin Bread" (*Science and Children*, Nov./Dec. 1975, Vol. 13, No. 3, pages 14-15.

31. Scattergrams

As a follow-up to histograms, you should ask another group of students to investigate the purpose and use of scattergrams. A scattergram plots the relationship between two measures; for example, height (in inches) compared to arm length (in inches). You can follow the same procedure suggested in activity 30. An additional concept in the use of scattergrams is called the "line of best fit." This concept is useful in helping one make predictions about the sets of data plotted.

32. Summarizing Data

A natural follow-up of the study and use of histograms and scattergrams is the use of measures of central tendency.

There are three measures of central tendency that small groups of students can learn to compute and use in minimizing a set of data.

A set of data—reading achievement scores, for example—have a *range* (highest to smallest score); a *mode* (the number that occurs most frequently), a *median* (the middle score when the data is ordered by size, arranged from low to high score), and a *mean* (the arithmetic average of the scores, obtained by adding the scores and dividing by the number of scores).

Using the data gathered from activities 30 and 31, have the

students find the range, median, mode and mean. Discuss with the students the advantages and disadvantages of each measure.

33. Picture Graphs

Provide a small group of students with one-quarter inch graph paper. Show this group how to graph a *number pair* (2,4). Point out that a number pair for a point is called its *coordinates*. Most math textbooks have an excellent explanation for graphing numbered pairs.

Once this group of students have mastered the concepts and understand the procedure for graphing number pairs (coordinates)—that is, that the first number of each pair indicates the point on the horizontal scale and the second number, the point on the vertical scale—have them try to make pictures similar to the one that follows:

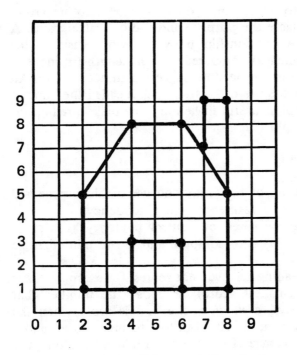

a) (4,8) to (6,8)
b) (4,8) to (2,5)
c) (2,5) to (2,1)
d) (6,8) to (8,5)
e) (8,5) to (8,1)
f) (2,1) to (8,1)
g) (7,9) to (8,9)
h) (7,9) to (7,7)
i) (8,9) to (8,5)
j) (4,1) to (4,3)
k) (4,3) to (6,3)
l) (6,3) to (6,1)

Have this small group make picture graphs for other students in class to plot.

34. It Takes Two To . . .

This activity can be completed by individuals or groups of students. Its purpose is to find the relationship between an ordered pair of numbers.

You can ditto a chart as follows or have students make up their own for other students to work out.

It Takes Two To . . .		
Pair	Number Relationship	Operation Relationship
3,2	6	product—multiplication
9,5	7	mean
8,7	78	reverse digits
etc.		

35. Word Puzzles

There are many ways small groups of students can use math word puzzles. This activity requires two students and two or more math textbooks.

The idea of this puzzle is to try to keep the game going as long as possible. The student who cannot think of a new math word loses (words of numbers—like one, ten, twenty are not allowed). Each student may refer to the math textbook only two times for each game.

Here's how it starts! The first student writes a math word. The next student uses one of its letters to add to it. Here is an example.

```
D E G R E E
I
G R O U P
I
T R I A N G L E
          Q
          U
          A
      L I T E R
             A
        P O L Y G O N
                 U
                 M E T R I C
                 E
               A R C
                 A
                 T
               V O L U M E
                 R
```

36. Word Problems

Have a small group of students observe and record ways students use math each day in and out of school. Have them do this for about three days.

As a result of this observation, have them design word problems that can be shared with their classmates. The group should be asked to include problems that encourage the use of equations to solve the problem.

37. Scale Drawings

Assign a small group of students the task of designing a city for people (approximately one thousand) who will be living on the moon. Have them use the metric system to complete this task. They should first plot out the plans on graph paper, using an appropriate scale (e.g. one centimeter represents five meters). If possible, let them then build their model moon-city.

Other small groups can be encouraged to do scale drawings on schools of the future, transportation for the future, new house designs, etc.

38. Challenge!

Give a small group of students a set of dominoes, a pair of dice, and one or more spinners.

Ask them to use their textbook to select concepts and principles that can be illustrated by each of these devices; for example, dominoes can be used to teach sets, ordered pairs, dice probability, etc.

Using these devices, have the group design student activities that will help their classmates learn specific math concepts and principles.

39. Weather Station

Have a small group of youngsters design a weather station for the class or school. Before they begin constructing their weather station, have them visit the local weather station and also have them write to the U.S. Weather Bureau (8060 13th St., Silver Springs, Maryland 20910) and the American Meteorological Society (45 Beaur St., Boston, Massachusetts 02108).

The group should make a list of instruments that are used and mathematical processes involved. Similarly, they should provide information to other students in the class regarding the Beaufort Scale, temperature readings using the metric system, etc.

40. Math Stories

There are several ways small groups of students can use math in writing their own stories or when studying the stories of others. For example, one group could write several one-page stories that replace the base ten numerals with a nondecimal base. They can have their classmates rewrite the stories using base ten numerals.

Another group of students can investigate the use of math in science fiction.

A third group may rewrite nursery rhymes substituting number phrases or bases for numbers in the rhymes. They can ask their classmates to solve them.

Another group can use a math textbook glossary and write poetry using the words in the glossary.